Malibu
IS BURNING

A Book Of Sextpoems By

MARK HAYES

Dedicated to The River.

EPIGRAPH

"This book saved my marriage."

MICHAEL RAPAPORT

FOREWORD

"Yeah, I don't want to do the foreword for the sex one."

ROBBIE WILLIAMS

INTRODUCTION

"Every night I read this book to my man and then we fuck."

TIFFANY HADDISH

RED DRESS

I walk into your room. You're sitting on the bed. Wearing a red dress. Just looking at me. You don't say anything. I walk over to the bed. You stand up. We're almost touching. You feel my breath on your neck. I feel your body heat. You unzip your dress. I slide it down. You're so fucking beautiful. I don't think you know. I kiss your neck. You moan for me. Let go. We look. Pause. Kiss. I grab you tighter to me by your ass. Run my hand through your hair. You're so fucking beautiful. You rip my top off. I push you to the bed. Slide your underwear down your long legs. Kiss my way back up. Tease your thighs. You're moaning. And so fucking wet. You want me to lick you. You want me to taste how wet. I slowly kiss your thighs. I feel your heat and hot wet pussy. You're so fucking beautiful. I run my tongue over your wet lips. You taste so fucking good. I'm licking you softly and sliding my tongue inside. Your ass is clenching. The bed is wet. You cum so hard in my mouth. You want me inside. You want me fucking you. Good girl.

GOLD DRESS

I want you to greet me at your door. Wearing your gold dress. As you turn and walk back inside, one strap slips down your shoulder. Your beautiful back gets me hard. You pause and look over your shoulder at me. I come behind you. You feel you have me hard already. Kiss your neck and caress your ass through the sheer dress. I lift it up to squeeze your perfect round ass. You're not wearing any underwear. You have me so fucking hard. You slide the other shoulder off and your dress falls down your waist. You let it slide down your legs as you walk inside naked. I take off my t-shirt and jeans as I follow you to the dining room table. You stand at the table, just in your heels. Your body has me so hard, your perfect ass, your tattooed back, your sexy legs. You lift your ass cheeks as I come behind you. I kiss your back and feel your breasts from behind. Slide my hard cock between your legs, teasing to see how wet. I get to my knees and kiss the back of your legs and thighs. Slowly kiss to the middle and taste how soaked you are for me. You put your hands on the table and lean forward as you feel my tongue taste your tight pussy and slide inside. I slowly lick from your trembling pussy to your ass. You want me inside. I stand back up and rub my cock outside your wet pussy. You stand up straight and run your hands through my hair and I feel your hard nipples and beautiful breasts. I guide you to the wall and press you against it, your hard nipples pushed up, your ass against me, moaning as I slide my cock inside your wet pussy. You feel so good. You're so hot. My cock feels like heaven inside you. You're pushing hard against me as I fuck you from behind. Spanking your ass. You're moaning and biting your lip the harder I slap. I grab the back of your neck and feel your pussy get tighter on my cock. You want me to cum. I want to feel your pussy on my cock as you cum. We waited so long. Your ass shakes and legs tremble. As you cum I grab your hips and cum hard inside with you. Fuck. You're so hot. You're breathing hard as I pull out. You stay leaning and bent over against the wall. You wait for me to dress and go. I hear the door lock behind me as I'm outside still tying up my belt. You hot fucker.

GOLD BIKINI

"Follow me," you say running down the beach. We go around the corner where no one can see us. I grab you close and kiss your beautiful lips. You're so fucking sexy. Your ass and legs feel amazing. You always turn me on too much. "Come," you say, taking off your bikini top. You have the sexiest body. You walk to the inlet and look back at me. "Strip for me." I do. You have me so hard. You face the wall and slide your bikini down your legs, grabbing your ass. I come from behind and you moan as you feel my hard cock slide between your legs to tease your wet pussy. I kiss your neck and feel your perfect boobs, playing with your rock hard nipples as you grind back on my cock. I can feel how wet you are on me, wanting me to slide inside and fill you up. You take my hand and put it on your neck. I start to squeeze as you play with my cock, sliding it inside your wet pussy. You moan, "Oh fuck. Yes, baby," at me as I go inside of you. Malibu is burning. It's sad. So sad. But you are the hottest fucker I've ever seen. I turn you around and you climb on me, wrapping your beautiful legs around me as we fuck, your wet pussy sliding up and down my hard cock. You start to cum as I kiss your nipples and fuck you deep. Malibu is burning as I cum inside of you. So sad. So harny. So fucking hot.

RED EYES

I catch you looking at me reading. "What?" I ask. "Do you think I'm weird looking?" you enquire. "No, you're the most beautiful fucker that's ever been." "Fuck you," you tell me, thinking I'm lying. "Fuck you," I tell you back, because I'm not. "Wrestle me," you say, like a demanding fuck. "What?" "Wrestle me, bitch." You knock the book out of my hands and push me. I push back. You jump on my lap and grab my cock. You already have me hard. Your eyes are so fucking beautiful. Your fucking lips. Outside, Malibu is burning. So sad. But you have me so hard. You lift your dress up and touch yourself, then put your wet fingers in my mouth. You're so fucking sexy. You push me again. "Wrestle me." I grab you and we tangle to the floor. You're a strong fucker. You get on top and pin me. Your eyes are brazen and you're stroking my cock outside my jeans. You really are the most beautiful fucker I've ever seen. "Wrestle me." I flip you over and pin you to the floor. I'm on top of you and feel how wet your pussy is. You're breathing hard as I feel you get wetter. My hand is on your neck, squeezing. "Harder," you tell me, pulling out my cock and stroking it. "Harder!" I choke you harder and you smile at me. Harder and you gasp for air, sliding my cock inside your wet pussy. I choke you hard and grab your sexy ass as we start fucking. Outside, Malibu is burning. So sad. But you cum hard and then I cum inside you. Poor Malibu. Miss Malibu. Miss you.

BROWN HAIR

You come out of the bathroom and say "Look." I put down my book and look. The blonde is gone. "I'm brunette again. Do you like it?" "I love it," I tell you. You look so pretty. "You preferred the blonde," you say. No, I like the blonde but like the brunette more. You drop your towel. You are the sexiest woman I've ever seen. Your body blows my mind every time. Your long legs and tattooed arms, and fuck me, your glorious boobs. You climb on the bed and crawl up my legs, asking what I was reading. As I try to answer, you take my hard cock and slide your lips and tongue up and down it slowly. You always get me so hard so quick. Outside Malibu is burning. We can smell the smoke. It's sad. You look out the window then start sucking my rock hard cock. You ask, "Do you like my hair?" "Fuck yes," I moan, as you make my cock even harder and wetter. You're so fucking sexy. I love your lips. You climb up me and kiss me. You're a sexy fucker. You smile and bite your lip as you take my cock and slide it along your wet pussy. You start to moan a little as you tease yourself with my cock. Your hand is on my chest as you slide my cock inside deeper. Fuck me, you feel amazing. Your breathing gets deeper as you grind your hips and ride my cock. Hand on my chest as you fuck me, rubbing your clit, grabbing your nipples. Your ass is clenching as you grind deeper and harder on me. You're in control and so fucking wet. Your ass clenches and body shakes as you cum on top of me. You ask me if I'm going to cum. Fuck, I am. You climb off and suck my cock as I cum hard, shooting down your throat. Jesus Christ. You make me cum so fucking hard. You lie on my chest as I play with your hair. Outside Malibu is burning. It's sad. So sad. But I like your new hair.

RED THONG

"Come outside," you tell me. You know I'm late but you want me to fuck you. You're wearing the red underwear that you know I love. It's a different bra. You never care that it doesn't match. Your wet hair is in a towel as you look over your shoulder. "Come," you tell me. Your ass is perfect, like a trophy sitting on your long sexy legs. As I walk outside to the balcony you turn around and undo your bra. You have the sexiest fucking body. I love your breasts and the cold air has your nipples hard. You're fucking perfect. The sky looks orange. Malibu is burning. It's sad. I pull you close and feel your body against my chest. You look so hot. Your beautiful eyes looking into mine. We pause and slowly kiss. It's Sunday. You love making me late. Your soft lips and wet tongue have me so fucking hard. Unzipping my jeans as I feel your wetness. I tease your clit and slide a finger inside as you stroke my cock, running your finger over my precum. You moan as I slide another finger inside, your towel falling to the floor. I love your brown hair. You look at me and stroke my cock faster. You're so fucking sexy. Dripping wet. "Fuck me," you moan. I pull you tight as you wrap a leg around my waist. You feel so fucking good as my hard cock slides inside. Soaking wet. I love fucking you, it fucks me up. You love my cock, bulging inside you. You cry, "Oh fuck," as you cum, your ass tightening and your pussy throbbing. "Cum for me," you say, your mouth open and soft lips hanging, looking for air. I kiss your lips and cum hard inside you. Fuck, you're so good. The air is dry but you're so fucking wet. Malibu is burning. I'm late. You laugh. I leave.

PINK THONG

I wake up and you're kissing my stomach. It's 5 AM. "I woke up sad," you say. "What's wrong?" You don't answer. It's because of Malibu. I know, so sad. I'm still half asleep as you slide your tongue along my cock. Two licks has me hard. I look in the mirror and see your ass in a pink thong. Jesus, that fucking ass. You kiss the top of my cock with your big wet lips then run your tongue back down. You take it all in your mouth. Fuck me, feels so good. You give the best head. Your mouth is wet and sliding on my cock, stroking it and looking at me. I pull you up and you straddle me. You're so fucking beautiful. I look in your eyes as you slide my cock along your wet pussy. Your lips want it inside. As you slide it in I feel your perfect ass. I fucking love your legs and ass. Kissing your neck and grabbing your hair as you get wetter and wetter on top of me. Your pussy feels so good. I love fucking you, feels like heaven. Your body sweating on mine. Your boobs pressed against my chest. You look at me and arch your back. I love hearing you curse as you get close to cumming. Oh fuck. I remember the time by the beach we fucked on the hood of your car. You came so hard. My cock gets even harder and your pussy feels tighter as your ass clenches and you cum on me. I keep fucking as you're cumming. You press your body on mine again. I feel the sweat on your back and grab your ass as you grind again up and down my hard cock. You're so fucking wet. I cum so fucking hard inside you, then on your ass. You lay on me, breathing deep. Malibu is burning. It's sad. But fuck, that was hot.

BLACK THONG

You arrive home. I'm trying to write, drinking tea. You're wearing that long black dress that has just one shoulder strap. I love your neck. The collarbone. What's it called? I forget. Your beautiful face. Fuck, you're so fucking hot. "How was your work?" You shrug. Tired. Malibu's burning. It's sad. "What's the name of the collarbone again?" I ask. "Kiss it," you tell me. Come. I take your hand and bring you to the bedroom. I look at your face. You're so pretty. I don't think you know how beautiful you are. I kiss your soft lips as you close your eyes. Your shoulders relax. I slowly kiss your lips, your neck, turning your head as I kiss behind your ear and unzip the back of your dress. You let the shoulder slide down and it falls to the floor. Fuck me, you're so fucking hot. You're standing in a black thong and your black boots. I've never seen a hotter woman. Your boobs are perfect. I kiss your neck and run my lips down to your nipples. They're hard in my mouth as I softly kiss them. You feel me guiding you to the bed. I slide your boots off as you lay back, feet on the floor, me on my knees. You close your eyes as you feel my lips kissing your legs, slowly up to your thighs. I slide off your thong and you're already wet. Your lips want me. I kiss your thighs slowly, spreading your legs as I get closer to your pussy. You moan as you feel me tease you, breathing on your clit, and running my tongue along the lips. I lick around your clit and feel you breath deeper. I slowly run my tongue along your lips and slide inside. You're so fucking wet. You push my head and my tongue goes deeper inside. I taste how fucking sweet it is. You're the hottest fucker. You're dripping wet into my mouth, wetness running down your thighs. My tongue fucking your pussy, teasing your clit, sliding my finger inside. You're soaking wet as I slide two then three fingers in, your clit hot and swollen as I run my tongue up and down, driving you wild. I keep licking and fingering until I feel your ass starting to shake slightly. My tongue slides up and down as your body starts to shake and you moan louder and louder. "Oh fuck," you keep saying, "fuck, don't stop." You bite the pillow as I bury my tongue in your soaked pussy, your clit so fucking hot and swollen. "I'm going to cum," you moan as your pussy pushes into my face, my tongue pushing back as your whole body shakes. You cum hard as I eat you out, ass grinding up and down. Soaking and dripping to the bed. I'm so fucking hard. "Fuck me." I slide my cock inside your warm, drenched, tight pussy. Fuck. You kiss my lips as we fuck. You're so fucking wet. We're sweating and your nails are clawing at my back. The heat of our bodies and your wetness are too much. I cum hard inside you, shooting deep, then take out my cock and cum hard again. You love it all over your boobs. You look at me as I'm holding my cock and smile. I can smell smoke outside. Malibu is burning. It's sad. "The clavicle," you say. Oh yeah, you smart fucker. That was hot.

BROWN BIKINI

I come to your house and you're by your pool. "Hello beloved," you say as I walk in, laughing. Your hair is wet and you're lying by the side. "I'm already wet," you tell me. "What are you doing?" I ask. "Listening to the guns." Malibu is burning. People are looting. It's sad. But you look so fucking beautiful. Your wet brown bikini, your wet brown hair, your beautiful brown eyes. You look at me then smile. "Come for a swim." You walk into the pool as I strip naked. I forgot shorts. Fuck it. You swim to the side and lean over the edge looking back at me. You have the nicest ass. It's so perfect. I'm hard by the time I'm in the pool. You're looking over your shoulder and sliding your wet thong off. I swim over and rub your sexy ass. Spreading your cheeks. Fuck, you're so hot. Your back arches as I kiss your ass and taste between your legs. You're wet and taste so fucking good. You have the sweetest tasting pussy. Your breathing gets deeper as I lick your lips and clit, feeling you get wetter. You breathe sharply then turn around and face me. "I like your wit," you tell me. I laugh. "I like yours," I tell you. "Say something Irish." I'm so fucking hard and dumb for you. "Potatoes." You smile and swim towards me. You're fucking beautiful. Your hand takes my cock and strokes it as we kiss in the pool. I love feeling your body. Your wet boobs on me, my hand on your wet back. I grip your neck as we kiss harder. You slide my cock inside your tight pussy. Fuck, you feel so warm and wet. I'm rock hard inside you. We move to the side and start fucking, your legs wrapped around me, my hand grabbing your ass, the other choking your neck. "Fuck me," you say, looking me dead in the eye. Fuck. You're my dream girl. You're your dream girl. Your pussy is gripping on my cock as I get harder and harder, my hand squeezing tighter and tighter. You hot fucker. You arch and lean back as I choke and fuck you. Your mouth opens for air and your beautiful lips hang. Your eyes go wide and you bite on your bottom lip. You start to cum as I squeeze your neck tighter, looking at me in the eye. Fuck me, it's too much. I cum hard inside you. I pull you to me as I cum more. Our lips lost kissing, a sea of sex, you're a beauty. You wrap your legs around me and we just look at each other. "I like your lips," I tell you, "and Jesus your cheekbones." "I know you do," you say, swimming away smiling. I hear a gunshot. Malibu is burning. It's sad, so sad. But you're naked and wet, and so fucking hot.

BROWN EYES

Fuck. You're beautiful. You're in the shower. I'm brushing my teeth and looking at water run down your body. Your wet brown hair and big pink lips. You look so innocent. You look so beautiful. Water runs down past your eyes, along your nose and drips off your lips. Your boobs are so fucking sexy. I love you naked and wet. Outside there's smoke. Malibu is gone. It's sad. But now I'm hard. And you're looking at me, with those big brown eyes. They're brown on brown on brown. You like me watching you soap up your body. Rubbing your nipples and stomach and over your pussy. You open the shower door, "Aren't you supposed to be making me breakfast?" "Yeah," I laugh. You're a fucker. "Kiss me first," you say, puckering your wet lips. I go to kiss and you pull me inside. I had just dried off. My towel falls to the floor as we kiss against the shower wall. Fuck. You're so fucking hot. We kiss hard. Your lips. Your neck. Your hard nipples. Water running down your body. You run your tongue along my ear, "Taste me."

I grab your neck and kiss your lips, then follow the trail of water down to your stomach and thighs. Kiss your soft skin and spread your legs. You stop me as you turn around and arch your back, bending over and looking back at me. I kiss the back of your legs and ass. Taste how sweet you are. The most beautiful girl. You taste so fucking good. I stand up and slap your sexy ass, teasing you with my cock. Your ass grinds on me as my hard cock slides along your pussy and between your cheeks. I pull you up and press you against the wall, hand on your throat as I slide my throbbing cock inside. You gasp as I go deep, your nipples hard against the wall, on your toes, pushing back against me. I love how wet you are, our bodies hot and dripping. Your pussy feels so fucking good. My cock rock hard inside of you. You slide it out and turn around to face me, wrapping a leg around me. I slide inside you again as you lean back, pressing against the wall. I'm lost in your body and how good your pussy feels. This is heaven. Outside people are looting. But fuck. You're the sexiest woman that's ever been. You push up and wrap both legs around me as I press you against the wall. Fuck, you start cumming as I kiss your nipples. I feel your pussy tightening as you finish cumming and moan for me. I cum inside you at the same time and stay hard, still fucking you. Fuck, I cum so hard. I still have you held up against the wall. You look down at me with your big beautiful eyes. You're the dream. You smile. "Make me breakfast." You're a fucker. I like it.

BLACK TOP

You're half naked sitting on your rug. "Where are my pants?" you ask me. Like I have a fucking clue. You're moving apartments and your bed is gone. Malibu has burned. The air is bad. It's sad. You're just wearing a black top. Long sleeves. Bare ass and legs. How are you so hot. I want to tie you up. You always wanted to fuck me on your rug. "Hang on," I tell you. I grab two of your scarves. You lie back on the rug. You know what to do. You look at me in silence and stretch your arms above your head. You're so fucking beautiful. I tie your hands together tight with one scarf then kiss your lips softly. Run my fingers over your neck and down your body. Your nipples are hard. I kiss your stomach down to your pussy. You spread your legs and want me to taste. I kiss your thighs and around your pussy. You moan as you feel my breath on your clit. I kiss closer and closer to your wet lips, teasing you as your ass slowly grinds up and down. You want my face buried between your legs, my tongue inside your tight wet pussy. I run my tongue along your thigh, then grab your feet and tie them together. Tight. You're mine. Tied on the rug. Now I taste how wet you are. You've the sexiest pussy. I'm licking your clit and running my tongue up and down your lips. "Fuck me." I'm so hard for you, opening my jeans. I take out my cock and you open your mouth for it. I let you suck it, your mouth and tongue wet and hungry. You want me wet and rock hard inside you. You deepthroat and gag on my cock, looking at me as I pull it out. My cock is dripping with your spit. You lick it and look me in the eye, then deepthroat again. Fuck, you're so fucking hot. You gag and let it slide out, pausing and looking at me. I turn you over on your hands and knees, still tied together. You look over your shoulder at me. I spank your ass hard and you hold in a moan. Again. Same cheek. Harder. You hold another in. Third time. Red cheek. Hard. You moan "Fuck," as I sting you. You're a hot fucker. I rub your ass and clit. You moan and bite your bottom lip. I spank hard again and you say, "Fuck you." Spanking hard again. Your knees almost buckle. "Fuck me," you tell me. I slide my cock inside your drenched pussy. Your legs are tight tied and your arms are trembling as I fuck you hard, going deeper and spanking your ass red raw. Your legs and body are shaking. You want to cum. I rub your clit. Grab your ass. Choke your neck as I fill you up. You moan and cum hard, your arms shaking and giving way. "Fuck me," you say again. I feel your pussy tighten and fuck you harder. I cum hard inside you, Jesus fuck, your body feels amazing. Christ. We lie on the rug. "My pants are in the bathroom," you say with a smile. I go to get them. Malibu is burning. It's sad. So sad. But I have your pants.

You hot fucker.

ALL IN BLACK

You show up to my show. We were just texting. Never met. Just texting. We texted all day for three days. You're so fucking beautiful. But your brain has fucked me up. You're a true feck. Your eyes are dancing. My brain wants to dance with yours. I want to kiss your lips. You look fucking hot. Dressed in all black. Black on black. The show is packed. People are sad. Malibu is burning. It's bad. I'm up next. You say hi in the hallway. Our first hello. Jesus, I'm turned on with you so close. We texted about everything. I want your brain. I want your body. Your lips are so fucking hot. You say hello and we hug. Your bottom lip hangs. I want to kiss it. You look at me. With your big brown eyes. They dance. We must kiss. I look at the bathroom. You smile. We go. It's empty. We go to the stall. Lock the door. Fuck me. You're so hot. It's hanging between us. We kiss against the wall. Pull back. Laugh. Kiss hard. We both had a drink. I taste it on your lips. Our breath is hot. Your lips are wet. Your hands reach under my top. Feel my body. Nails grab my back. I feel your body. Grab your ass. Bite your lip. You gasp. Look at me. Bite your lip. Slide your pants down. Slowly. Looking at me. Reach for my belt. I undo it. Unzip my pants. I'm so fucking hard. You look at it and smile. Stroke it and then go to your knees. Your wet mouth on my hard cock. Fucking Jesus. Feels so good. I'm so hard. You suck and take it all in your mouth. Deep. You pull it out and look at me, spit still on my cock and your lips. You suck my balls and stroke it, then suck again. Fuck. I'm already close. You know. You stand up and lean against the wall. Pull your underwear down. My turn. I kiss your legs. Your sexy thighs. Your pussy is wet. I can feel it. Breathing on your clit. Licking it. Slowly. It's throbbing. You moan as I barely lick it. Teasing you. It's so swollen and wants my tongue. I lick and slide my tongue inside. You're so wet. Your pussy is so sweet. You grab me and turn around. Look

22

over your shoulder. I slide my hard cock inside. Fucking you from behind. Trying to keep in moans. Trying to be quiet. I'm grabbing your ass. I want to spank your ass. I stand you up and fuck you against the wall. You start to cum on my cock, gasping. I cum with you, hard. Shooting inside. Fuck. They're calling my name. We're still fucking. I turn you around. We kiss and I'm still hard inside you. It's a charity show. Malibu is burning. It's sad. But fuck. I want to keep kissing you forever.

LEATHER DRESS

I'm on my way to the gym. It's cold. I'm in shorts and a t-shirt. I can smell smoke. Malibu is burning. It's sad. You text me. You just got home. I just missed you. "Come back," you text me, with a photo of you in your black leather dress. Jesus, you're beautiful. I could look at you all day. I want to kiss your big beautiful lips. "At the gym," I tell you. "Come," you text, with a photo of you in just your underwear and boots. Jesus Christ. You're the devil. The dress is gone. You're in a black thong. I'm getting hard. Fuck. I want to get naked with you. "After," I tell you. "Come," you say, "I'm horny now." You text me a photo of your ass in the thong. Jesus, your ass is perfect. You're fucking perfect. I'm waiting to cross the street. I'm hard. In shorts. Fuck. You're the worst. "Come," you text, "I'm wet." A photo of you pulling down your thong. "Alright," I say. It's not far. "What do you want me to do?" you ask. "Get on the bed naked and be waiting. I want you to touch yourself for me. Feel your clit and how wet you're going to be for me when I get back. I want to walk in and you're dripping for me." You send me a photo of your naked body. Fucking Jesus. You're the dream. I want to kiss you all over. I'm so fucking hard. Trying to hide my hard cock as I go back home. When I get to the apartment you're on the bed. Sitting up. Your boobs are so fucking sexy. Your face is so pretty. You're fingering yourself and rubbing your clit, just like I told you. Fuck. My clothes are off. I'm naked and rock hard for you. I get on the bed and get on top of you. You're still fingering your wet pussy. I rub your clit as I kiss your lips. Fuck. I love kissing you. Your clit is big and throbbing for me. Your pussy is so wet. I kiss your lips and your neck. I want to taste how wet you are. Running my lips down your body. Sucking and licking your nipples. Kissing your stomach. Down to your shaved pussy. You're so wet as I slide my tongue along your lips. Running it over your swollen clit. You start moaning hard as my tongue slides inside. Soaking wet and warm. I start licking your lips and suck on your clit. Your ass is clenching hard. It's wet from your pussy. I lick it and your legs slide open wider. Run my tongue over your clit. Your ass is off the bed as I flick and lick my tongue over it. You grab my hair as you moan louder and louder. "Oh fuck yes," as you cum while my tongue is inside. "Fuck me." I take my hard cock and slide inside. Fuck. You're stupidly wet and warm. You're beautiful. You're looking at me in the eyes as I'm fucking you deeper and deeper. Harder and harder. Spanking you. You bite your lip. Harder. I spank. You moan. You bite. I spank. Harder. Spank. Put my hand on your neck. Kiss your lips. Feel your sweat. Choke your neck as you start to cum again. Oh fuck. You're so fucking hot. Malibu is burning. It's sad. But you're the most beautiful girl I've ever seen. I start cumming too. Shooting deep inside you while looking in your eyes. You gasp for air. I kiss your lips. Fuck. You're beautiful. We lay there. You look at me and smile. "You can go workout now." You're the fucking devil. I like it.

DENIM JACKET

I look over and see your face. You light up the room. Fuck. You're beautiful. We're at a bar. It's busy. Laurel. Charity event. Malibu is burning. It's sad. Save the animals. I'm stuck talking to a guy talking at me. You're stuck doing the same. I look over and see your pouting lips. Your sexy neck. Fuck, your neck is so hot. I like your hair tied up. Black dress. Your denim jacket. Your knee high boots. You're a fucking supermodel. Everyone has been looking. Even the kitchen staff came to see how beautiful you are. I saw them while I was looking at you too. True creep. You look and smile at me. Come kiss me. You walk over and save me from this little man. "Hi." "Hello you hot fucker." You smile and wrap an arm around me. You smell good. We should have fucked before we came. We were late. I want to fuck you now. You seem to know. You slide your hand under my top and run it up and down my back. Nails on my skin. You squeeze hard. You're a fucker. I smile out the pain. You want to fuck. "I need the bathroom," I say. You take my hand. The bathrooms are shared. Three doors. All busy. It's just us. Waiting in the hallway. You look in the mirror at us then grind your ass against me. You can feel I'm hard. You always have me hard. You smile and bite your lip. I like looking at us in the mirror. I like fucking you in front of the mirror. You take my hand and slide my fingers under your dress. You're so wet already. Fuck. You get me even harder. It's bulging against my belt. You're rubbing my cock as I'm fingering your wet pussy. You're breathing hard and closing your eyes. You're so fucking hot. I forget where I am. I put my hand on your neck. Just squeeze lightly. You want more. I squeeze tighter. Sliding your hand inside my pants. Stroking my cock. It's so hard and throbbing for you. Your pussy is so wet and ready for me. I rub along your clit and feel it getting bigger. Fuck. I want to fuck you right here. You open my belt. Grab my cock. Slide it inside your dripping pussy. Jesus Christ. You feel fucking amazing. You grind back and take it all inside. Fuck. We're just grinding. Can anyone see? I don't fucking care. You're so fucking sexy. It's dark. You start grinding up and down my cock more and more. I'm squeezing your neck and grabbing your perfect ass. You're the hottest fucker. I'm fucking you from behind. You're keeping in moans, like a good girl. You feel so warm and wet, I love it. A door opens and you quickly stand up straight. It's dark. A famous actor. He doesn't know. He's on his phone. We slide inside. My jeans fall down. You turn around and sit on the sink. Oh my God, you're fucking beautiful. I kiss you hard. Jesus, your lips. I fuck you on the sink as you wrap your legs around me, lifting you up. You're soaking wet as you slide up and down my cock. Your legs squeeze around me tighter as you cum on me. I cover your mouth as you cum then you kiss me hard. You're dripping down me. "Cum for me," you say. I grab your ass tight and fuck you against the sink. "I want it," you say, dropping to your knees ready for it. I look at you in the mirror and cum hard in your mouth. Fucking hell. You take it all and look at me, then stand up and smile. You kiss my lips and pull your dress down. I feel fucked stupid. Dizzy. Light headed. Delighted. I like it. Someone tries to open the door. Oh yeah. We're at a bar. Malibu is burning. It's sad. I just want to stay with you in here all night though.

BLACK BRA

I wake up and you're looking at me, "Good morning." "Haha how did you get in?" "I took your key." Oh yeah. I like that you're just wearing a black thong and black bra, lying on your stomach, up on your forearms, ass in the air. Fuck, how are you this hot. You're just looking at me still, figuring me out. "What's this ting?" you ask, holding up a stick next to my bed. "Are you doing an Irish accent?" "Maybe. What is this ting?" "A shillelagh." "What's that?" "An Irish stick." "That's dumb." I laugh and grab the stick while wrestling you onto your back. Pin your arms down by the side of your head. "What are you going to do?" you say trying to fight free. "Fuck you," I tell you. Your lips smile but you wrestle and try harder. Malibu is burning. It's sad. But you're a strong fucker. I pin your arms tighter to the bed and squeeze your body with my legs. You're going nowhere. We kiss hard. Your wet lips feel good. Fuck. You're hot. My body is pressed on yours. You feel the weight. Dominating you. I brush the hair from your eyes and look at your beautiful face. You're a vision. You take your free hand and reach for my cock. You look me in the eyes as you slowly stroke it up, barely touching it. Fuck, I'm rock hard for you. I feel between your legs. You're wet through your thong. You sexy fucker. I rub your swollen clit and watch you bite your lip. You're a good girl. I slide a finger inside your wet pussy as you stroke me, running your fingers along the top of my cock. I tease you and rub my finger along your lips. Finally your eyes close and you moan. You're so fucking wet. Your ass is grinding as I finger your wet pussy and tease your throbbing clit. You keep getting wetter. You reach for my wrist and I slide another finger in. You open your eyes and look at me. You want to cum. You're close. Your mouth is open. Silent. Moaning. Gasping. Closer. Cum for me. I'm so fucking hard watching you. Feeling how wet. I squeeze your neck as your pussy tightens and ass clenches. You cum as I squeeze harder, moaning and grabbing my arm as your body tries to twist. I still have you pinned down. You look at me and pull me close. You want to be fucked. We kiss hard as I slide my cock inside. Fuck. You're like an ocean. It's so fucking warm. You're so fucking beautiful. Your pussy floods on my cock as we fuck and kiss. I grab your neck and your back arches. You're a good girl. Fuck. You grab my ass and pull me in "Cum for me." I'm lost in you. I cum hard inside you. Feels amazing. Fucking Jesus. You're a hot fucker. Malibu is burning. It's sad. But you're looking at me. And smiling. I like it. I like you. Until you pick up the shillelagh and hit me with it, laughing. "Get your tings," you say, "we're late." You're a feck.

BLACK TIGHTS

"I don't want to go," you tell me. "Well, you must," I laugh. It's a charity fashion show. For Malibu. It's burning. Save the birds. "Why won't you come?" you ask. "I have a show too." "Well you can model and I'll do comedy. I'm funnier than you." "I know," I tell you, looking at your pouting lips. "Make me happy before I go." "How?" You're dressed in all black. Black jacket, black top, black skirt, black tights. You're beautiful. You're funnier. And the most beautiful. It's very odd. "Suck my ass," you say, pouting your lips and batting your eyes. "Haha really?" Can't tell if you're joking. "Really," you say, as you pull me in and we kiss. The door is open. Neighbours might see. Fuck it. I get lost kissing you. "Suck my ass," you say in my ear. "Turn around," I reply, now kissing your neck and running my tongue to your ear. Are you serious or joking? You pull back and look at me, then turn around. You're not joking. You put your hands on the new mirror I bought and look over your shoulder at me, spreading your legs apart. Fuck. You're a hot fucker. I pull up your skirt and rub your ass. You've the hottest ass. Give it a spank. Hear you moan. You're a good girl. You look at me in the mirror. I pull your tights down your long legs, then kiss your ass cheeks. Kiss the back of your thighs. Rub your ass and feel if you're wet. You're so fucking wet. You sexy fucker. I kiss your thighs and pretend to bite your ass cheek. You moan as I run my tongue over your ass and between your legs. I taste how wet you are. It's so sweet. You taste so good. Thank God we had pineapples and potatoes for breakfast. You start touching your clit as I slide my tongue inside your wet pussy. "Suck my ass," you say again. I look at you then slide my tongue along your ass. You love it. My tongue teases and flicks over your sexy ass. You moan and close your eyes. I spread your cheeks and lick inside. You moan and rub your clit more and more. I tease your ass and taste your wet pussy, then slide inside your tight ass again. "Fuck," you moan. I look up. Door wide open. Neighbours might see us. Fuck it. They hate us. I slide my tongue in deeper and grab your thighs. Your cheeks are clenching and your arms are struggling to keep hold on the mirror. I can feel your pussy dripping down to your ass. "Fuck me," you say, "fuck me." I keep licking and sliding my tongue inside you, rubbing your swollen clit as you moan louder and louder. I'm fingering your dripping pussy as my tongue pleases your ass. "Oh fuck, I'm gonna cum," you say, rubbing your clit too. You cum hard and moan loud, my tongue inside you still. "Fuck me," you say again. The neighbour's door locks. I stand up and you turn your head over your shoulder. You kiss me hard. You're a hot fucker. Your wet lips feel so good. You bend over more as I slide my hard cock inside your soaked pussy.

Fuck. You feel amazing. My cock is rock hard and throbbing now. About to explode. You sense it. "In my mouth," you tell me. I cum hard in your mouth as you're on your knees. Fuck. So hot. You swallow it and smile, then stand up and kiss me again. "You should brush your teeth," you say, pulling up your tights. You're a fucker. "Now I can go to the show." Oh yeah. The charity show. Malibu is burning. It's sad. The birds. Weird they didn't just fly away. Jesus. I look at you again smiling at me. You're amazing.

BLANKET LINGERIE

Thanksgiving. I'm late. I was at a charity thing. Malibu. It's burning. So sad. I show up. House in the hills. Everyone is drunk. Everyone ate. I see you. You're so beautiful. In your low cut top. Looks like lingerie. Your boobs look so sexy. Wearing a jacket and sweats. You're a hot pikey. I want to kiss your lips. I don't know what's going on at this house. Everyone is drunk. Having fun. Sleeping. I'm hungry. Would love a potato or some sort. Jesus, you're the hottest fucker. You're sitting by the fire. Alone. I'm already hard. I want to see you naked. You see me and say "Lock the door." I do. You start touching yourself as I walk towards you. You're so fucking hot. Your tits are so sexy. You feel your nipples. Hard as fuck. Your lips look so good. I kiss you as you sit up by the fireplace. I love your mouth. You take a blanket and put it over me. Your wet lips kiss me hard as you sit on me, blanket over us. You unbuckle my pants and take my hard cock out. I slide your pants off and your lingerie comes down. We're both naked. Under the blanket. People are around. The door is locked. I'm so fucking hard for you. You grab my cock and slide it inside your wet pussy. You're dripping wet already. Your pussy is ready to cum on me. You start to ride my cock. Slowly. I can feel how swollen your clit is. Rubbing it as you ride me. You're dripping wet on my rock hard cock. I love how wet you are. Fuck. You ride me slow then fast. Your sexy ass grinding up and down. You're a good girl. I grab your neck and squeeze as you ride my wet cock harder. You love it. You sit up on my cock. Blanket is on the ground. Your wet pussy dripping. Sticky on me. You're sweating. I love your back. Grab your ass as you grind on me. Sitting up straight on it. Rubbing your hard nipples as you moan more and more. "I'm gonna cum," you tell me. Fuck. You're so beautiful. I rub your clit as my cock fills you up. "Oh fuck," you moan biting on your lip. Your body shakes and your hand is on my chest. "Fuck." You cum on my hard cock. I feel it dripping on me. I kiss your nipples in my mouth as we keep fucking. My wet lips on them. You love me kissing them. Malibu is burning. It's sad. But you're dripping wet on my cock. I love it. Happy Thanksgiving.

KNEE HIGH

We're at the Grove. It's your birthday. I don't know why we came here but we're here. You're still sad. Malibu is burning. So sad. But you look beautiful. You always do. But today so fucking hot. In your little dress and knee high socks. Leather jacket. Your nipples are hard. You're the best. "It's my birthday," you tell me. "I know," I say. "I'm horny," you whisper in my ear. I know. I can tell. You smile and look at me. Then pout. We're at a quiet part of the Grove. Killing time. Waiting for the cinema. You look at me again and kiss me. Your wet lips. Your warm mouth. You're a sexy kisser. It's Sunday. You're wet. I can tell. You take my hand and slide it between your legs. "Feel me." I do. You're dripping wet. Fuck, your thong is soaked. Now I'm hard. Cock bulging against my belt. "Taste it," you tell me. I slide my finger inside your wet pussy and watch your face as you bite your lip. "You're beautiful," I tell you. "Why do you say that all the time?" you ask. "Because you are. The most beautiful. And I won't be able to say it when I'm dead. So I say it now." I'm rambling as I'm fingering your wet pussy and teasing your clit. People are around. We're in the open. The Grove. But no one knows. You're a good girl. You're keeping in moans and trying not to close your eyes. You're so wet, I love it. I'm softly teasing your clit and you moan deeper. Louder. I pull you closer and kiss you. "Don't moan," I tell you. You smile. You like it. Your clit is throbbing. You're dripping. People walk by and we smile at each other. Then you kiss my neck and pull at my ear. "Fuck me," you say. I laugh and rub your clit. I like you in a dress. I can feel your wet pussy on your legs. I want to make you cum in public. It's your birthday. Your leg is moving. You're getting closer. I'm so hard against you. You want to taste my cock. Feel it on your lips. Inside your wet pussy. I want to taste how wet you are. I can feel how hard your nipples are. Your boobs feel amazing against me. Your clit is so swollen and ready. You bury your face in my shoulder as you cum, biting me. Fuck. You're a sexy fucker. Your ass is twitching. Your thong is soaked and my hand is so wet from you. We go to the bathroom in Nordstrom and fuck in the cubicle. No one comes in. You lift your dress up and I slide my rock hard cock inside you. You feel amazing. Warm and wet and perfect. You're a good girl. You look me in the eye as I cum inside you. We kiss hard as you feel me shooting deep inside your warm pussy. Fuck. You're hot. It's sad. Malibu is burning. But it's your birthday. We just both came. We're going to the cinema. You're beautiful.

CUTE HAT

I get back to my place and you're waiting for me. We haven't seen each other in a while. You've been away. Working. Busy. It's been good though. I've missed you. "Hi," you say to me, sitting on my new table, "have you missed me?" "No." I lie, as you stand up to greet me. You're wearing your favourite black top, Biggie and Tupac, and your cute hat. You smile at me. Your big beautiful lips. You look so hopeful when you smile. You hug me and I smell how good you are. I kiss your long sexy neck. Your arms are on my shoulders as you look at me with your big beautiful eyes. My hands are around your waist as I hold you close to me. You start rubbing against me, knowing you can get me hard. "Are you hungry?" you ask. "I'd love some porridge," I say. "I'm hungry," you tell me, kissing me as you feel my hard cock through my jeans. Fuck, you're always the hottest. We kiss hard, your tongue teasing me and making my brain dance with delight. Malibu is burning. It's sad. I'm hungry. I'd love some porridge. But you're busy unbuckling my belt and pulling out my hard cock. You look at me and smile, then take my cock and lick from the base to the top. "Have you missed me?" you ask again. "Oh fuck yeah," I moan as you take my hard cock in your wet mouth. Jesus. I'm in heaven already. You have me rock hard and my cocking dripping wet. The door is still open. The neighbour might see. But fuck it. You're playing with my balls as you swallow my cock. So wet and so hard. I want to taste your wet pussy. You already know. You stand up and take your jeans off. I watch you undress as I stroke my cock. You yank your tight jeans off and stand in front of me in your t-shirt and thong. You're the most beautiful fucker I'll ever see. I kiss your wet lips and slide your t-shirt off. Fucking hell. Your boobs and body are amazing. You're heaven. I kiss your neck and hard nipples as you sit up on the new table. It's brown. It almost didn't fit in the door. Can't tell if I like it. I like you sitting on it. Your legs spread. Naked. Looking at me hard. I kiss your stomach and your thighs, then taste your sweet pussy. Your pussy is the sweetest. Your clit is swollen and throbbing as I lick my tongue up and down slowly. We haven't fucked in a while. Your pussy is waiting. You're getting wetter as I lick your clit and slide my tongue inside your lips. You moan as my tongue slides in and out, then up along the side of your clit, then slowly along the top, over and back. I keep licking until you're dripping down your legs. Fuck. You're beautiful. I love your long legs. I want them wrapped around me. I watch you rub your clit for me as my tongue is inside you. You start to cum in my mouth and I keep licking. "Oh fuck don't stop," you moan. I keep licking and touching your clit, then stand up and slide my rock hard cock inside your warm wet pussy. Fuck. You feel like the dream. I love looking at you. Touching you. Fucking you. Watching your mouth. Moaning. Gasping for air. Cumming again on my cock. My hand squeezing your neck as you cum hard. "Cum for me." You look me in the eyes and bite your bottom lip. Oh fuck, I'm cumming too. I shoot deep inside your tight pussy and watch your eyes smile, then pull out and cum on you. You smile more and rub my cum on your hard nipples, then lick your fingers. Oh fuck. You're ridiculous. Malibu is burning. It's sad. But I like the table now. Let's have some porridge.

BOOTY SHORTS

"What are you doing?" I hear you ask. "Trying to write a joke," I say, without looking up. I'm on my balcony. Struggling to write. "Do you like my shorts?" you ask. I look up. You're in small denim shorts and a white bra. Fucking hell. You're so hot. "I do," I tell you, "I like you and your shorts." "I had an awful day," you say. "What happened?" "Nothing." Malibu. It's burning. So sad. I take you by the hand and lead you to the bedroom. You undo your bra as I sit on the bed. You want me to see how beautiful you are. Fuck, your body is insane. Your beautiful lips. Your sad eyes. I kiss you and hold your back, pulling you close. You kiss me hard and release, your eyes closed and lips wet, hanging in the air. You feel my cock outside my pants, already hard for you. Your boobs are so fucking beautiful, hard nipples wanting me to kiss them. You back away and turn around looking over your shoulder, "Do you like my shorts?" I'm so hard and dumb for you. "I do," I say and you start grinding on my cock. Slowly rubbing your ass up and down on it. Your sexy thighs rub against me and you sit on my cock, grinding on it. I want you naked and me naked. You step forward and slowly slide your shorts down your legs, looking over your shoulder at me. You're so fucking hot. I open my pants and take out my cock as you slide your thong off. I can see your wet pussy teasing me. You lapdance on me, slowly grinding your ass on me, teasing my hard cock along your wet pussy lips, dripping on me. You back into me again as I grab your ass and spank your cheek. You like it. You're a good girl. I kiss your red cheek and the back of your thighs. I run my tongue along your wet pussy and slide it inside. You burst open, wetness dripping. You start moaning and feeling your nipples and I lick your pussy up to your clit. You want to turn around and slide on my hard cock. I grab your ass and eat your pussy from behind, me sitting on the bed, you bent over in front of me. You're dripping on me, you taste so fucking good, I love feeling your legs shake and your ass clench as your clit gets bigger and more turned on. I rub your clit as I slide my tongue inside your ass. You've the hottest ass I've seen. It's magical. The magic ass. I bury my tongue back in your soaked pussy. Fuck, I want my cock inside you. Your vibrator is on the bed. I turn it on and rub it on your clit as I lick your pussy. "Oh baby," you moan, "More." Your clit is so big and you're so fucking wet. You stand up and sit on my lap as the vibrator drives you wild, my hard cock pressed against you, my hand on your neck. You're grinding hard against my cock as I squeeze your neck tighter. Good girl. You start to cum on me, ass clenching hard as you cum, vibrator driving your clit crazy. "Fuck me," you say, "I'm your good girl." You turn around and sit on my rock hard cock and start riding it. I'm choking your neck and kissing your hard nipples as you fuck it so good. You are my good girl. You start cumming again as I grab your ass and spank you. Fuck, you feel amazing. I cum hard inside you. Fuck, you feel so good. You kiss me again and I feel how wet you are on my legs. You're the hottest fucker. You take a breath and smile at me. Malibu is burning. It's sad. But fuck, that was hot.

RED ON RED

Just as I get to the gym you text me. I swipe my card and walk in reading it. You hot fucker. A photo of you naked under a sheet. I took it this morning. You're so beautiful. Your big eyes and your perfect big wet lips. You have the nicest boobs. I knew you were going to be the most beautiful before we even met but in person you're next level. Seeing you naked is insane. Makes me happy. Malibu is burning. It's sad. But you naked cheers me up. Woke up this morning to you under the sheets sucking my hard cock. Thought I was dreaming. You looked up at me when I woke up and smiled, then kept sucking. So fucking hot. Your wet lips kissing and licking and sucking my hard cock and balls. I started cumming as you were stroking my cock and licking my balls. You put my cock in your mouth and swallowed my cum. Felt like a dream. I'm just standing in the middle of the gym looking at your text of the photo I took of you under the sheets. With your beautiful boobs and hard nipples. I now realise I'm fully hard at the gym. Wearing soccer shorts. Not good. I pretend to tie my lace. Still hard. Make my way over to the stretching area. Trying to hide how hard I am for you in public. You text again. "I see you. I like you hard." You're here. You fucker. You text me a photo again. You in your red workout gear. Tight sports bra and little shorts. Fuck. Stop getting me so hard. I see you walking towards me smiling. In red with a grey hoodie. You're sweaty and look beautiful. "Hi," you say, laughing at me. You know you have me so turned on. "Hello fucker," I reply, pretending to stretch and tucking my hard cock along my waistband. Now I can stand up at least. "Help me with something in my car?" you ask. I'm all yours and you know it. We go downstairs in the elevator. You're standing close to me and rubbing my cock with your hand. Two others in the elevator with us. I don't even care if they know. You parked underground. In the corner. It's quiet. You flash a smile at me and bite your lip. I see your nipples are hard through your top. You look sweaty and beautiful. Fuck. I want you on me. We get in your jeep and I sit in the passenger seat. You look around and then take my cock out. Covered in precum. You lick it off your fingers while sliding your shorts down. You rub my cock again and slide your wet fingers inside your pussy while looking at me. Fuck. I can hear how wet you are. You take your fingers and lick them, then kiss me. You're a sexy fucker. "I'm so horny," you tell me. You don't say. I'm covered in precum, stroking my cock, in a car park. "Me too," I laugh back. You straddle me and I kiss your lips, down your neck and tease your hard nipples. Damn, you're dripping wet already. "Fuck me," you say, sitting slowly on my cock. Oh fuck, I slide inside you and it feels so good, your wet pussy on my rock hard cock. You're the hottest fucker. My hand is on your sweaty back, you're grinding your ass on me, I'm rubbing your clit, you're holding the roof, I spank your ass, grab your neck and kiss your lips. I rub your clit as you slide up and down and grind on my cock. "Fuck," you moan at me, mouth open, wanting more, cumming as I choke your neck. You're a good girl. Fuck, I cum with you, shooting inside. I cum so hard for you, I feel dizzy. You sit on me and kiss my lips. A car beeps in the distance. You laugh and jump off me. Malibu is burning. It's sad. But fuck. You. You're something else. I must go work out my glutes.

BLACK TOP & THONG

It's Sunday morning. I'm reading a book and about to go to the shop. Must buy some fruit. Maybe some persimmons or some plums. We had nice plums in Malibu before. It's still burning. So sad. You just woke up and walk into the kitchen. You're in a black top and small black thong. You're almost too hot. I'm turned on every time I see you. Can't even go to the gym without getting hard if you pop in my head. A true deviant. "Where are you going?" you ask. "To buy some plums," I say. "I want you first," you tell me. "No," I say. I really want those plums. "No?" you ask, turning around and standing on your toes. Arching your back. Showing me your perfect fucking ass. Fuck. I want to bite it. "Fuck me again," you tell me. We fucked all night. You need more. You see that I'm hard already for you. Cock bulging in my jeans. "Go to the bedroom," I tell you. You walk to the bed and climb on top, kneeling and facing forward. Your handcuffs are next to the bed. You're already waiting with your hands behind your back. You're a good girl. I put them on and rub your ass, then spank it hard. You moan loud. It's early. Your silk scarves are by the bed. I put it one over your mouth and tie it up. I take the second one and tie your feet together too. You lie on the bed looking at me. Your pretty eyes and gagged mouth. You're fucking beautiful. Then I leave. I walk to the shop down the streets. They're out of persimmons. I buy three plums. I'm turned on the entire time thinking of you tied up on the bed. Waiting for me. I'm rock hard buying plums. I walk back slowly. I put the plums on the counter and pour a glass of water. You look open as I enter the room. Your eyes are on fire. You're turned on and pissed I left but you like it. I take your gag out and ask if you want water. "You better fuck me good," is your answer. I flip you over face down on the bed. Your thong is soaking. Your pussy is so wet for me. You love being tied and gagged. I kiss your pussy from behind, tasting how sweet you are, teasing your ass, rubbing your cheeks. I start rubbing your clit softly as I slide my tongue inside, listening to you moan. You're dripping for me. You want to be fucked. I'm so hard for you. I start fucking you from behind, slapping your sexy ass, as you moan and grind your ass up and down. You're still tied up and your body is sweating. I love your sexy back. My cock is deep inside your soaking pussy. You're beautiful. Your clit feels so big as I reach around and rub it. I pull you to your knees and fuck you kneeling. Hand on your neck. Squeezing as you moan on the gag. You spit it out as you start cumming on my cock. Fuck. You're so hot. I love your sweaty back against me. Your hard nipples. You cumming on my cock. I cum hard as we keep fucking. You love me cumming inside you. I can feel it dripping down us. I untie the scarf and take off the handcuffs. You turn around and suck the cum off my cock. You swallow what's left. You're a good girl. I lie on the bed and look at you kneeling next to me. You're so fucking beautiful. "Did you get plums?" "I did." You smile. Malibu is still burning. So sad. But fuck it. We have plums.

ARMY GREEN JACKET

"Meet me for a drink," you text me. You don't even drink. But you need one. "OK let's booze," I reply. You must be sad. Malibu is burning. Worse ever day. An earthquake in Alaska too. So sad. We meet at a bar by my place. I order vodka sodas and wait. You walk in looking chic. Black pants. Black turtleneck. Army green jacket. I like your necklace. You hot model. We drink. And chat. And laugh. Your lips are beautiful. I like being around you. Your eyes. They light up. We talk. And drink. And kiss. You're sitting closer to me. "I'm fucking wet," you say in my ear, then feel for my cock. You smile when you feel how hard I am for you. "I want you to taste me," you say. Let's go. We Uber to mine. We kiss. And feel. And get lost. You're fucking beautiful. I like kissing you. We kiss in the kitchen and you turn around. You want to be spanked. Your ass is so nice. I spank you through your pants. "More," you say. I spank again. "I want you naked," I tell you. You laugh when you see two plums on my counter. You take them and walk to my bedroom. I watch as you undress and on your hands and knees on my bed, wearing just your red thong. You know what you're doing. "Spank me," you tell me, then put a plum in your mouth. I strip to my boxers and kneel behind you on my bed. I look at you in the mirror. Fuck. You're unreal. Such a hot fucker. You're on your hands and knees, plum in your mouth, waiting to be spanked. I rub your right ass cheek and spank, hearing you moan. I rub and spank again, harder. You moan again, juice running down your chin. I spank your ass harder and you moan and bite on the plum. Your ass is red already. Your mouth is filled with plum juice as I slap your left ass cheek. I can feel how wet you are through your red thong. It's soaked. I peel it down your thighs and slide it off your legs. Your pussy looks beautiful, so pink and tight and wet. I kiss your red ass cheeks and your thighs. You moan hard on the plum as I taste your wet pussy. Fuck, you taste so good, it's like a strawberry. You're moaning and arms are shaking as I lick your pussy and play with your clit. It's throbbing and you keep getting wetter. My tongue is sliding inside as I look at us in the mirror. Your mouth is dripping with juice. You bite on the plum and start to cum as my tongue is deep inside, your legs and arms shaking as you moan for me. You're a good girl. "Fuck me," you say, "fuck me." My cock is throbbing for you. You turn around and look at me. You're beautiful. Your sexy lips. You throw the plum to the side and pull me close. I slide inside you as we kiss, fuck, you feel amazing. Your pussy is so wet and warm on my cock. "Choke me," you say as I fuck you. I squeeze your neck and look in your eyes as my cock slides in and out of your soaked pussy. Your mouth stays open and you gasp, then bite your bottom lip. You're a good girl. You grab my wrist to squeeze harder. Fuck, you're unreal. I start to cum as you look me in the eye, shooting deep inside you. Your eyes light up as you feel me cum hard. You smile and grab my ass, pushing me inside even more. My body is on top of you, pressing against your hard nipples. I came but you still have me rock hard. We keep fucking. Slowly grinding. Deep inside you. Cock rock hard. Pussy dripping wet. You reach for the other plum and take a bite, then kiss me. "Eat it out my ass," you say, looking at me with a smile. Fuck. Malibu is burning. It's sad. But fuck it. I'm eating a plum out of your ass.

RED BIKINI

"What are you doing?" I ask. "Trying on bikinis." "It's December." "I know," you say, "and I'm cold." It doesn't make sense, but it does. You look beautiful. In your red bikini. I haven't seen that since we went to Malibu last. It's still burning. So sad. Fuck, your body is amazing. Your tight stomach. Your toned legs. Your beautiful arms. I like your arms. You're a weapon. Your beautiful neck. Your hair covering your boobs. "Where are you going?" you ask. "That meeting I have." You pout. Your beautiful lips. You bite the bottom one. You know it turns me on. You come closer to me and rub my cock. You like me being hard for you all the time. You kiss my neck and feel me get harder. You're a fucker. I hold the back of your head and pull you away. Jesus, you're beautiful. Your big eyes asking me to fuck you. You undo the bikini top and let it fall to the floor. Fuck, your hard nipples look amazing. I have to kiss them. I kiss your lips and your neck, then push you back onto the bed. I climb on top of you and feel your neck in my hand. I run tongue down your body and over your hard nipples. You moan for me as I kiss and gently bite them. I need to keep going and taste you. I kiss your stomach slowly down to your shaved pussy. I slide your bikini bottoms down your legs. You're soaking wet, I'm rock hard. I kiss inside your legs up to your thighs slowly, spreading them as I make my way to the top. You're breathing deeper for me, waiting for me to taste you. I like teasing you. Running my tongue along your clit so little you barely feel it. Breathing on it as I kiss the side of your pussy. Knowing you're getting wetter. Knowing you want me. Sliding my tongue inside your pink lips and filling you up. You taste so sweet. You're so wet, like a juicy plum, or a wet potato. I'd love a plum. You're dripping down your legs to your ass. I follow it and tease your asshole. You moan louder and clench as I slide my tongue inside. I grab your ass cheeks and kiss my way back to your pussy, then lick your clit. It's throbbing for me. You're getting louder and louder on the bed as I run my tongue up and down it. You grab my hair and then the sheets as your ass lifts up. You want to cum. I want to taste it. I slide my tongue inside you, then kiss your clit. You grab my hair and cum hard in my mouth. "Fuck." I love you cumming. You're so fucking beautiful. I climb on top of you and kiss your beautiful lips. I look at you and squeeze your neck, watching your face as my rock hard cock slides inside. Fucking hell. You feel like heaven. So wet and warm and tight. You wrap your legs around me and push me deeper. You're biting your lip and gasping as I squeeze your neck. Your eyes light up as I fuck you. You look at me and smile, then moan hard as you cum more. Your pussy gets so wet and tight on my cock as you cum, fuck, I cum hard with you. I shoot inside then you open your mouth and put your tongue out. I take out my cock and cum on your boobs, then on your lips and tongue. You start sucking my hard cock, licking the cum off. You're beautiful. You rub some cum on your nipples then lick it off your fingers. "Yum," you say. "I'm going to get a plum," I tell you, "Want one?" You do. Malibu is burning. It's sad. So sad. I missed my meeting. It's bad. But you're trying on bikinis. And we're eating plums. That's fun.

LITTLE BLACK SHORTS

Fuck. I'm dying. We just did hot yoga. You finally came. Had to be on separate sides of the class though. I didn't want to see you. You would've had me too turned on doing it. In your tight black sports bra and tiny black shorts. Had me hard on the way there. The heat and sweat made it go away at least. Now we're both dripping sweat. Class was tough. "My body is on fire," I tell you. You look sad as you look at me. Forgot. Malibu is burning. So sad. "You look beautiful," I tell you. You do. You're glowing. You can't take compliments. But you smile. "Let's shower," you say. I'm still rolling up my mat. I watch you leave and walk to the men's changing rooms. Ha. You're unreal. I follow you in. No one else is here. We start kissing in the changing room. Your lips are so beautiful. Big and soft and wet. Fuck. I'm rock hard. Your nipples are even harder through your top. You pull it off over your head. I take my t-shirt off. We're both drenched from the class. Our bodies look hot. You slide your black shorts off as I do the same. We're naked in the changing room. Anyone could walk in. You don't care. You stroke my hard cock as we kiss, naked. Fuck. I love your lips. I feel your breasts and hard nipples. You close your eyes as I kiss your lips, my hand around your sexy neck. I want to fuck you right here in the middle of the changing room. You push back and look at me, biting your lip. "Fuck me," you tell me. "Go to the shower," I tell you. I watch you go to a stall and turn the water on. You let it hit your face and run down your body. You look at me as you slick your hair back and rub your nipples.

You trace a finger down your stomach and slide it inside your pussy for me. You're a good girl. You taste it and smile. I join you under the water and close the door. You're so fucking beautiful. The water reminds me of Ireland. The rain. The fields. My cow. Daisy. You kiss my lips as our bodies press against each other. I'm so fucking hard. You drop to your knees and take my cock in your mouth. Fucking hell, you're ridiculously good at sucking my cock. You look up at me while sucking my balls and stroking it, water dripping down my body as you look me in the eyes. You're a hot fucker. You stand up and turn around, bending over and spreading your legs. You want me inside. I want to taste first. I kiss your back and ass, they're both perfect. I slap your ass and rub it, hearing you moan. I kiss your thighs and slide my tongue inside your wet, warm pussy. You're drenched for me. You taste so sweet. I feel your clit, it's so big and swollen. Fuck. I want you. I stand up and slap your ass again. "Ugh! Fuck me," you say. I slide inside, filling you deep. You moan loud and push back, making me go deeper. Your hands on the wall, bent over, me sliding deep inside and slowly out, feeling your pussy get tighter on my hard cock. Fuck, you feel so good. You take your right hand and feel your boob, then start rubbing your clit. I'm grabbing your hips and fucking you deep. You're moaning deeper and deeper for me. Your ass is grinding on me. My cock is deep inside. You're rubbing and moaning, "Oh fuck baby," as you're close to making yourself cum. "I'm cumming. Fuck," you moan way too loud. Jesus, you're hot. You cum hard and hang onto the wall. You turn and kiss me hard, then wrap your legs around me. My cock is so hard inside you. I'm fucking you against the wall, lost in you, your wet body, your wet neck, squeezing, hearing, feeling you. I pick you up and you bounce on my cock. You look at me with your beautiful eyes and we kiss hard. You cum on me and I start cumming deep inside you. Fuck me. You're ridiculous. I'm lost. Still inside. Cumming hard. We stand kissing, me holding you, your legs wrapped around me, water raining down. Fuck. That was hot. We wait until someone leaves the changing room and dry off. We fuck again in the car downstairs in the car park. Malibu is burning. It's sad. I miss daisy. But we should do hot yoga more.

BLACK BIKINI

I'm at the dining table, trying to write, eating a banana, drinking tea. Thinking about Malibu. It's sad. Still burning. Never ends. You stroll in the door. Back from the pool. Dripping wet. In your black bikini. Hair slicked back. You look fucking hot. "I love December in LA." "Very Christmassy alright," I say. I pretend to ignore how hot you look and type out some words. I can hear your wet bikini and hair dripping on the floor next to me. You waiting for me to look. "Tell me I look good," you say. I drink some tea. Type another word. Feel myself getting hard before I even look. You take the banana out of my hand as I'm about to bite it. I finally look. Fuck. You're so fucking hot. Your body is tanned and wet and I can see goosebumps. "You look fucking beautiful," I tell you. You smile and sit on my lap facing me. Your bikini is soaking. You wrap your arms around my neck and kiss my lips. I love your lips. Wet and soft and full of joy. You feel my hard cock through my pants and smile. "Oh you like that?" you ask. Fuck yeah I do. You grind your ass on me and feel me get harder. You wrap your legs around and pull yourself closer. Everything is wet. Your boobs are in my face while I'm looking at your lips. I want more, you hot fucker. You take the banana and have a bite, then grind on my cock. I undo your bikini top and pull it off. Your nipples are wet and hard. Your boobs are so sexy. Glistening. You smile at me as I kiss your hard nipples. Your eyes close as you moan. I hold your back as I kiss and softly bite on them. Your hand reaches for my cock, unbuttoning my belt and opening my jeans. "I want to taste." You slide off and get on your knees under the table. You pull my jeans open as you kiss my balls and stroke my cock. I hear you spit on it as you kiss and lick it slowly. Fuck, you have me so fucking turned on. You take my hard wet cock and start sucking slowly, taking it all in your mouth. I hear your gag under the table and keep sucking.

My cock is dripping in your spit as you deep throat and stroke it slow, then fast. "I love it," you say, then take it in your mouth again. I look down as you look me in the eyes while sucking. You start touching your pussy while looking at me. Gets me even harder. You're rubbing your clit and sucking my cock. Fuck me. I want you. I pull you up and you sit on my lap, rubbing your throbbing clit along my hard cock. You're so wet too. Kissing your lips as we tease each other. I stay seated and turn you around. Your hands are on the table. Bent over, glancing back at me over your shoulder. I'm rubbing your ass and looking at your sexy pussy. "I want to taste it," you say, handing me the half eaten banana. I rub it along your pussy and clit. Is this what bananas are for? Sorry, God. You take the banana and look at me, then eat it and taste how wet you are. Fuck. I start to lick your wet pussy from behind and get harder as you moan. My tongue is sliding between your lips as I rub your swollen clit. Your ass is clenching as my tongue goes deeper then slides up to lick your clit. You're grabbing your boobs and pushing back against my mouth. "Fuck me," you say, and sit back on my cock. You slide me inside you and moan, grinding on my cock and looking over your shoulder at me. I feel your sexy back and pull you closer. I rub your clit with one hand and squeeze your throat from behind with the other. "I'm gonna cum," you say grinding harder. I'm so hard and you're so wet on me, your ass slapping off my thighs. I feel you cum and get even harder. I grab your ass and fuck you deeper. I cum inside you, shooting hard, almost biting on your back. You keep grinding and fucking me while I stay hard and shoot more. "Let me taste it," you say, climbing off and getting on your knees. I cum into your mouth and on your lips. You smile and look at me while you lick my cum, then swallow it like it never even happened. You stand up and finish the banana. Jesus. Malibu is burning. It's sad. But fuck. That was so hot. I need a swim.

BOOTY SHORTS

We're strolling to Trader Joe's, going to stock up on fruit before Christmas. You're drinking a pint of milk as we stroll. "Why milk?" I ask you. "I like it," you tell me. "I wish I had a bucket of it." You take a swig from the bottle and your lips go white. You stand in front of me on the street and look me in the eyes, then kiss me. Your wet milk lips. You pass milk into my mouth and I swallow. You're a feck. "See, it's good," you tell me. You're a fuck. Now I'm turned on. You were sad all morning. Malibu. It's burning. So sad. And you were at a funeral. They always make you horny. So sad. Now you're smiling again at least. Wearing your tight long sleeved black top and little booty shorts. You look hot. You walk ahead of me drinking milk. Your ass looks so sexy, like a ripe persimmon. I want to tap and spank it. You seem to know. We're on Fountain, no one else around. You take me by the hand into an open parking garage. I pin you against the wall and kiss your milky lips again. Your bottom lip is dripping and juicy. "I wanna fuck you and then go home and eat porridge," you tell me. I lift you up against the wall as you open your booty shorts and pull them down. You grab my hard cock and open my jeans. You want to suck it but we don't have time. "Just let me taste it," you say. You drop to your knees and lick my cock, then start sucking. Fuck me, I love when you deep throat. You slide it out of your mouth, hard and drenched in your spit. You stand against the wall, hands on it and shorts pulled down. I rub and slap your ass, then feel your wet pussy. Teasing it with my cock. You moan for me as I slide inside you, filling you up. Fuck. You're so tight and wet. Your pussy explodes on me as we fuck, getting wetter and wetter as I'm harder and deeper inside you. I pin you against the wall as you stand on your toes. Your pussy sliding up and down my hard cock, dripping down my balls. You're rubbing your clit as I grab your ass and hold your hair. I cover your mouth as you start to cum on my cock, fuck, you feel amazing. I'm lost fucking you until we hear an alarm go off and voices coming. Fuck. We stop and walk back outside. Nothing happened. Jesus Christ. I'm so hard for you I can't even

think. You forget your milk, then go back and get it. You're so
horny still, you want more. I take your hand and we walk to
Trader Joe's. We're too turned on to talk. Can't even look at each
other or we'll fuck on the street. We get to the store and walk
inside. I grab a plum going past the fruit section. We go straight
to the bathroom and lock the door. You turn around and lock
eyes with me. We're fucked. You straddle me as I lift you up.
My cock slides inside your soaked pussy. I can feel your cum
still. You take the plum and put it in your mouth as I lift you up
sliding you down onto my hard cock. I like looking at us fucking
in the mirror. You're a good girl. You're biting on the plum and
gripping me tight. You cum again on me, moaning into the plum
and juice dripping down your chin, your pussy dripping down
my cock and balls. Someone knocks at the door. Fuck. Again. I
don't want to cum yet. We tidy up and walk outside smiling. We
leave and quickly walk home. Too turned on. "I want porridge,"
you tell me. "Me too." We get back to the apartment and start
kissing in the kitchen. I try to make porridge. I don't know why.
You start sucking my cock as the porridge is almost done. I take
it out of the microwave and pour milk on it. Fuck. I need to cum.
You're on your knees on the kitchen floor. You open your mouth
and ask for a spoon of porridge. I feed you a spoon and you start
stroking my cock. You're so fucking hot. You start sucking me
with porridge in your mouth. Jesus. I cum so fucking hard as
porridge drips down your chin. You suck and swallow my cum
then take it out and I cum again on your lips and chin. You smile,
licking the porridge and cum. Malibu is burning. It's sad. But
you're a deviant. I like it. We must go buy fruit.

YOGA PANTS

I'm in my Uber on the way back from LAX. You text me a photo
of your ass in your new yoga pants "Do you like?" you ask. Yes
I fucking do. The Uber driver asks if I'm ready for 2019. "No,"
I tell him. He looks at me and turns up the radio. Malibu is

burning. It's sad. Everyone is sad. Your ass photo just turned me on though. "Show me without the pants," I tell you. You show me. Fuck. Your ass is amazing. Those cheeks. I want to bite them. "Be waiting in the kitchen," I text you. "OK." You're a good girl. I get back to the apartment and open the door. You're in the kitchen wearing just a black thong. Cutting food. You look over your shoulder at me. Your back and ass have me hard already. "Try some broccoli," you tell me, popping some in my mouth. Pretty good. You eat a bit and turn around. You run a piece of broccoli down your body, slowly along your neck and between your boobs, then along your hard nipples. Jesus Christ, why is broccoli turning me on. I take it and eat it, then pull you to me. "Hi," you say, smiling your beautiful smile. We kiss as I lift you onto the kitchen counter. You undo my pants as I feel your wet thong. You're soaking. I like it. I pull your thong down your legs as you put them on my shoulders. Fuck, your pussy looks amazing. Pink and wet and tight. I want to taste it. I kiss your smooth legs and slowly spread them apart. Running my kisses along your thighs. You lean back as my mouth touches your wet lips, my tongue teasing them open then sliding inside. I love hearing you moan. You taste so fucking good, so fucking sweet. I run my tongue along your clit and slowly lick over and back. You grab my hair and get wetter in my mouth. Your ass is grinding up and down on the kitchen counter as my tongue teases and tastes you. I slide inside your wet lips then run it back over your clit. I feel you cumming as you grab my head and moan loud for me. Fuck, you taste amazing. We kiss as I lift you up and wrap your legs around me. I carry you to the bed and flop you on it. I get on top and pin you down. You look at me while stroking my hard cock. Your eyes are beautiful. You slide me inside and groan as I fill you up. Jesus, you're unreal. You feel so good on my cock, your wet pussy dripping down my balls. I squeeze your neck as I go deeper. You tilt your head and arch your back as I lift your ass up. You're so fucking wet, I love it. You start sucking my fingers as I fuck you. I want to feel your body on me. I flip you over as you climb on top. You look beautiful. Rubbing your boobs and riding my cock. I spank your ass as you grind faster and harder. "I'm cumming," you moan, grinding hard and holding onto me. I grab your ass and fuck you deeper, cumming hard inside you. I cum deep inside you again as I pull you closer to me, kissing your wet lips. I stay hard as you slowly grind on my cock, breathing deep on me. You lie on me then roll over and smile. Malibu is burning. It's sad. But that was hot. Good old broccoli.

RED

Sad day. I'm at Trader Joe's. They're out of persimmons. No longer in season. Malibu is burning. Mean Gene died. So did Marty Funkhouser. It's sad. But this is worse. I love persimmons. Sold out of plums too. I make my way home. You're in the kitchen. Slicing up a mango. Fuck, forgot about mango. "Try some," you tell me. Jesus, it's unreal. You're unreal. You look beautiful. Wearing your red gym outfit. Or is it a bra. I can never tell. You smell beautiful too. Your hair. I kiss your lips. So soft and wet with mango juice. You look at me, fuck, your eyes. We kiss harder. Running my hands through your hair. The mango kicks in. I'm hard. You're horny. It's hot. I squeeze your sexy ass and pick you up. You wrap your legs around me as I undo your bra. I kiss your hard nipples as I carry you to the table. You sit down and unbuckle my jeans. You slide your hand inside my boxers and smile, feeling how hard I am for you. We kiss as you stroke my cock, my hand on your neck, your lips tasting like mango. "I want to taste," you say. I stand back as you spit on my cock, then slowly lick from the bottom to the top. You slide some mango along my hard cock and take a taste. Fuck, you have me so turned on. You taste the mango off me then slide my cock inside your mouth, taking it all in. You gag as it goes deep, taking it out soaking wet. You stroke it looking at me, saliva on your lips. My cock is so hard and wet for you. You suck again as you touch yourself. I want to taste you. I stand you up and kiss your lips. You smile and grab my mouth, then spit in it. You're a bad girl. "Sorry," you say. "Too late." I take your bra and tie your hands together. I turn you around and bend you over the table. Your fucking ass. So hot. I slide your booty shorts down and rub your ass cheeks, then spank hard. You moan as your ass stings. I spank again as you moan louder. I spank again as your ass goes red, leaving a handprint. "I'll be good," you say. I spank hard one more time, your ass clenching as you moan even harder. I turn you around and lie you on the table, your hands still tied. I tie the bra to the top of the table and look at how beautiful you are. Your body is amazing. Your eyes and lips and neck and teardrop boobs. Your stomach and legs and your pretty pink pussy. It looks so wet. I get some mango and slide it along your pussy lips and clit. I put it in your mouth then take another piece and slide it inside you. You bite your lip and breathe deeper as I slide it in and out. I don't think God made mango for me to fuck you with but here we are. Sorry, God. You open your mouth to taste. I feed you the piece then kiss down your body. You moan as I tease your clit and slide my tongue inside. I eat your wet pussy and torment your clit with my tongue. I feel your tied hands reaching for me as you cum. "Fuck me," you say, with your legs wrapped around my head. I climb on top and slide inside you. We fuck on the table. I love looking at you. You're so fucking beautiful. I love dominating you. You cum again as your back arches off the table. I cum with you, shooting deep inside. I squeeze your neck and keep fucking you, then pull out and cum again on your boobs. Jesus, you're amazing. You smile and lay there, asking for more mangoes. Today was sad. No more persimmons. But that was hot. And you're a good girl. Sorry, God.

WHITE THONG

It's raining in L.A. Which is weird. Because Malibu is still burning. And they still don't have clean water in Flint, Michigan. It's sad. But I'm cold. And hungry. Eating some mashed potatoes and gravy. Love some gravy. You call me to the bedroom. I walk in and you're on your knees, on the bed with your back to me.

You look fucking hot from behind. Wearing your white thong. Your beautiful round ass. Jesus. Almost drop my potatoes. "Do you like my new underwear?" you ask. Of course I fucking do. "Yes you hot fucker," I tell you. You look over your shoulder at me. You're beautiful. I'm already hard. Was meant to be going to the gym after I finish eating. You spot my hard cock in my shorts. "Get on your hands and knees," I tell you. You do as you're told. I place my bowl of potatoes on your back. It's hot to touch and you like it. You open your mouth and I feed you a spoonful. Reminds me of feeding my cow Daisy back in Ireland. I miss her. She'd like this rain. You swallow the potatoes. You feel my cock as I start to rub your ass. You reach into my shorts and take it out "Hey big boy." So dumb, but I'm so hard for you. "Don't let the bowl drop," I tell you. You spit on my cock and stroke it slowly. I rub your ass then spank hard. You clench but the bowl doesn't move. I spank again harder and hear you moan. I spank a third time and you cry, "Fuck." You like it. The bowl stays on. I take it off and you open your mouth. Your wet lips and tongue on my cock as I reach to feel how wet you are. Your thong is soaked. Good girl. You spit on my cock again and stroke it slowly, looking at me. You keep looking as you wrap your lips around it and take it all deep in your mouth. You start choking on it then take it back out. You look at me with saliva on your lips as I put my hand on your neck. You close your eyes and squeeze my wrist to make it go tighter. I squeeze and run my cock along your lips. I tease your mouth then go behind you on the bed. Your ass is red. I spank your other cheek until it's the same colour. You're soaked. I kiss your ass and slide your thong off your sexy legs. You look over your shoulder then moan as you feel my tongue along your pussy lips. I run it along your clit, going slowly over and back on it. You moan as my tongue slides inside your wet pussy, tasting how sweet you are. You're a good potato. I feel you get wetter in my mouth as my tongue teases your lips and licks your clit. I lick to your ass and feel your legs shake on the bed. You cum as I eat you from behind, your wet pussy dripping down your thighs. You grip the bed as I keep licking. I love you cumming. I sit on edge of the bed and you sit on my lap. We kiss hard, wet lips on wet lips, bodies pressed against each other. You take my cock and slide it inside your pussy. Fuck, you feel so good, your tight warm pussy dripping wet. I'm so hard for you. Fucking you deep as you slide up and down my hard wet cock. I spank your ass as you bounce on me. You love sitting on my lap. I bite your neck as you feel my nails on your back. You're moaning loud. You're going to cum again. "Cum for me," I tell you. You grind harder on my cock as I pull your hair and squeeze your neck. You're so fucking beautiful. You cum hard, your body wrapping around me. I cum inside you deep, shooting hard. We keep fucking as we cum. Our sweaty bodies. Our wet lips. You sit and kiss me as we breathe deep. Jesus. Malibu is burning. Flint has no water. I miss Daisy. But that was fucking hot. You hot potato.

TRENCH COAT

We're on the east coast. Visiting your family. It's cold but nice. Brisk. We're strolling on the beach. Malibu is burning. The government is shut down. Brexit is a disaster. It's sad. So sad. But I like strolling with you. You look like art. Your hair in the breeze. Your big beautiful lips. Your eyes are even brighter out of L.A. You're the dream. You write my name in the sand. "Hi Mark." Hello sand. "Have you ever seen a baby seagull?" you ask me. "I haven't." I don't think. Maybe I have. I'm not sure. You look beautiful today. I can't stop looking. You flick some sand at me with your stick. I look at you. You laugh and do it again. I run and pick you up then wrestle you to the ground. Your body feels warm. It's brisk. I like it. I look at your beautiful eyes and kiss your soft lips. I feel some drops on my head. Sand? No. Starts pouring rain. Sweet Jesus. I lift us up and you twirl in the rain. You nut. Let's go. I don't want to get wet. You laugh and take my hand. We run up the beach getting soaked. There's a church nearby. You take me by the hand and lead me inside. It's beautiful in here. My old priest Father Joe would love it. We kiss inside the door and know it's wrong. Sorry, God. A door swings open somewhere. You take my hand and lead me along the aisle. We go to the confessional and slide inside. Fuck. We're going to Hell. Sorry, Jesus. I close the door and open your trench coat. Your hair is soaked and face is wet from the rain. We're two drowned rats. But you look so fucking beautiful. We kiss and I pull you close. Your body feels warm. Your nipples are hard. Fuck. You're a hot fucker. You feel my hard cock outside my pants and unbutton my jeans. I unzip yours and slide my hand down your panties. Your pussy is dripping. I rub your swollen clit as you stroke my cock. Your soft wet lips on mine, your tongue in my mouth, dancing with mine. You pull your pants down more and put a leg up on the confession chair. Sorry, Jesus. I grab your ass and pull you close, my rock hard cock sliding inside your warm wet pussy. You feel so fucking good. Your wet pussy sliding up and down on me. You start to moan so I cover your mouth. You squeeze my hand and I squeeze your neck. You like that. You're a good girl. You feel so fucking good. I grab your ass tighter. Oh fuck, you feel amazing. I want to cum inside you. I'm rubbing your clit as you moan louder into my hand. I feel you close to cumming. Cum for me. You moan hard and loud as you cum for me. I'm trying to muffle it. We hear footsteps and a knock at the door. "Is everything okay in there?" It sounds like an old lady, maybe a nun. "Yeah," I warble out, so close to cumming inside you. "I'm just praying," I say. "Okay, the priest will be along shortly." she says. Sorry, Jesus. "Thanks." I say, and then start saying 'Our Father', out loud. Your eyes light up and you kneel in front of me, then take my cock in your mouth. I keep praying out loud while you suck me slowly. As we hear the footsteps walk away, you stroke my hard wet cock and I cum in your mouth. Fuck. You're a hot fucker. Malibu is burning. The rain is pouring. I'm soaked. But that was fucking hot. So sad. You hot heavenly turnip.

BLUE DRESS

It's pay day. Happy days. For some reason I got paid for a show in cash. A big bag of money. Mostly quarters. Handy. I come home and dump them. Coins and singles all over the bed. A bed of money. Malibu is burning. A bomb went off in Northern Ireland. The government is shutdown. It's sad. So sad. But I have a bed of money. And I just ate a plum. I spot an empty bag of jalapeño chips on the floor. Macklemore is playing on the TV. Your sister must've been here. "Come here, feck." I call out. You're in the bathroom. You sound late. I walk in and see you sitting on the bathtub, shaving your legs, wearing your blue dress. It's my favourite. Goes with your eyes. You look so pretty in it. And it looks like you churn butter for some reason. Jesus. You're beautiful. Even with one hairy leg. "Where are you going?" I ask. "Editor of Sports Illustrated wants to meet about writing articles. Blah blah blah, I'm late." You finish shaving and stand up "How do I look?" You're beautiful. "Like the dream." You come and kiss me. Your soft wet lips. Your minty fresh breath. I love kissing you. I like your hair up too. You look cute, for a complete fucker. You get lost in the kiss and pull away, eyes closed, "Now I'm horny," you tell me. Now I'm hard. "Come," I tell you, leading you to the bed. "Look, a bed of money." You laugh and then realise it's a lot of quarters. "I always wanted to fuck on a bed of cash," you tell me. You crawl on the bed and lay down on your back. "I'm late," you say again. "I know," I say, as I slide my hand between your legs and up your dress. You wiggle your ass as I pull the dress up. You're not wearing underwear. You hot fucker. I kiss by your knees, then slowly up your thighs, my tongue and lips getting closer to your pussy. I hear you breathe deeper as my lips kiss your inner thighs, then run my tongue along your clit. You moan as I flick my tongue along it slowly, teasing it up and down, licking and feeling it get swollen for me. I slide my tongue between your lips and taste how wet you are. You have the nicest pussy. You reach for my head as I slide my tongue deeper inside. I love how sweet you are. My tongue sliding in and out, tasting your dripping pussy. Your clit is so big for me as

I slide my tongue up and down it slowly. You're moaning loud as I feel you grabbing the bed and quarters with your ass rising up. My tongue is flicking your clit slowly up and down, then sliding inside and feeling you gush. I keep licking your clit as you moan deeper for me. "I'm cumming," you tell me, breathing quick and ass shaking. I kiss your pussy as you cum and grab my head, my hands grabbing your ass. "Fuck. I wanna fuck," you tell me. I'm so fucking hard for you. I stand up and open my pants until you see the time. "I'm too late!" You jump up and kiss me, stroking my cock. "I want to fuck it so bad" you say, bending down to taste it. Fuck, that feels unreal. "I'll drive you to the meeting," I say, "Where is it?" "Chipotle." We take your Jeep. The windows are blacked out. You suck my hard cock as I drive down Sunset. You're a hot fucker. You're gagging as I pull into the parking lot, eyes watering like you've been weeping. I drive to the far side of the lot and you climb on top of me. We kiss hard as I pull up your pretty blue dress, then slide my cock inside your soaked pussy. You feel fucking amazing, riding my cock as I squeeze your neck. Your eyes are so beautiful, they look like the world. I'm so close. "Choke me," you say. I squeeze harder and start to cum and shoot deep inside you. Fuck. You're unreal. I grab your ankles as I cum again. You missed a spot shaving. One hairy ankle. I grab your ass as I stay hard and fuck you more. I shoot again inside you, then pull you close as we kiss. Your hair is still up. You look pretty. You fix your mascara and pull your dress down. Malibu is burning. Bombs are going off. The government is closed. But that was hot. I have a bed of quarters. And Sports Illustrated is going to love you, and your hairy ankle.

RIPPED BLACK JEANS

We're both at the same casting studio. I hate auditions. They make me mad. The world is burning. Hate crimes are rampant. Women are getting shot. It's sad. And in my last audition I had to kiss a teddy bear on the lips pretending it was a dog. They asked me to leave. I see you booking all the time. Although your pants just ripped on the chair as you sat down next to me, always a good sign. You're so beautiful. You look Irish. And South African. But American. And savage. And a weapon. And pretty. And sweet. All wrapped in one. And your ass is showing through your ripped jeans. Jesus Christ, you're unreal. You look at me and say hi. Hello you delight. "Heck, my pants are ripped so bad." You're so polite you don't even curse. Heck and gosh and darn. I want to kiss your red lips. And your nose. And your neck. And your beautiful body. "Is it bad?" you ask me, standing up and showing me your right ass check. "No, it's unreal," I tell you. Jesus, your ass is amazing. How are you so beautiful and so nice and now I'm trying to think of stuff so I'm not turned on in this full casting waiting room? "Do you like turnips?" I ask, like a fool. "Oh gosh, I love turnips," you say, "How did you know?" I always know a turnip lover, it's my only talent. You bite your lip as I'm looking at it, then go red. Fuck. We're both turned on by turnips. What are the odds? "How do you like yours?" you ask me. "Salted and roasted, and some garlic pepper," I say. "Garlic pepper is so good, if that's your thing," you say. That is my fucking thing, I want to say, then pick you up and strip you naked. "It is," I say instead. You bite your lip again and breathe a bit deeper. I can't tell if you're turned on but you have me, so now I'm going a bit light headed and getting hard just looking at you and smelling you so close and all this talk of turnip. Our bodies seem to be dancing while we just sit next to each other looking at our lips. "Gosh." "What?" "I don't know." "OK." "I'm flustered." "Me too." "I need to go see how bad my jeans are ripped." "Okay, the bathroom is down the hallway," I tell you. "Can you cover me as I walk, so people can't see my whole ass?" you ask. Oh fuck yes. I stand up and walk behind you down the hallway. I'm hard and you're walking slow, your ass bumping against my cock. I hear you breathe deeper as you go slower and feel it against you more and more. There's no one waiting for the bathroom but someone's inside. You stand in front of me, ass pushed against my hard cock. Your hand reaches for mine and I follow it to your bare ass. Fuck. Your ass is like a tender turnip.

I love it. I feel your ass cheek as your hand reaches and feels my hard cock. Fuck, I'm so turned on for you. You're grinding your ass against me and stroking my cock outside my pants. I'm rubbing your ass and feeling between your legs. Jesus, you're so fucking wet. You open my belt and pull my cock out. I slide your thong to the side and feel how wet you are. Fuck, you feel amazing. The toilet flushes and we freeze. A little old Canadian granny walks out the door and smiles, then potters up the hallway. You grab my hand and take me inside the bathroom. I lock the door as you turn around and look at me. "Hi." Hello hot fucker. "What the heck are we doing?" you ask. I don't know. But fuck it. I kiss your beautiful lips and lift you to the sink. You rip off my shirt and run your hands on my body, then stroke my hard cock, pulling it fully out of my pants. I open your ripped jeans and slide them down your legs. You look at me and smile, then close your eyes with my hand on your neck. You're beautiful. "Fuck me," you whisper in my ear, giving me chills. I slide inside your dripping wet pussy and feel your nails in my back. "Oh heck," you keep saying as I pick you up and fuck you against the mirror. Your pussy is dripping down my cock as I muffle your moans. You dig your nails into my back as you slide up and down my rock hard cock, dripping in your wetness, your clit hot and throbbing as I rub it. I grab your ass and slide you up and down, kissing your beautiful lips. "Oh daaaarn," you moan into my neck as you cum on my cock, then start fucking me harder. "I wanna taste it," you tell me, knowing I'm about to cum. You go to your knees and open your mouth, swallowing my cock as I shoot hard and cum deep in your throat. Oh fuck, you're unreal. You swallow it all and kiss my cock, then laugh and stand up. You're a hot fucker. You kiss my lips and pull up your ripped jeans. Malibu is burning. People are hating. Women are dying. But that was fucking hot, you hot fucking turnip.

STRIPY SKIRT

We're at a Chinese restaurant in New York. It's your friend's birthday. I don't know anyone. Malibu is burning. It's raining in L.A. Chicago is frozen over. But you look so savage, you beautiful fucker, in your black sweatshirt and stripy skirt. I can't stop looking at your face and lips across the table. I want to kiss you. Every day. Every time I see. That's the plan. You see me looking and smile. Fuck, your eyes are amazing. They light up when you smile. There's a guy next to me who I don't know. He's asking if I know any good classic rock songs. "Yeah," I tell him, thinking of the sex we had in the hotel earlier. You were watching 'The Blair Witch Project' and got scared. You kept your white runners on as we fucked on the bed. It was hot. Your beautiful body on mine. I'm turned on thinking about it. There's a table of women next to us reading out sex poems. Everyone in this restaurant seems horny. It's great. I want to kiss your face. I don't even know what I ordered. Some house special. Turnip stew. Sounds great. You love turnips. I want to fuck you now in the bathroom. Lift up your long skirt and feel your ass. I feel a foot under the table. I hope it's not classic rock guy next to me. I look at you smiling at me. You look so beautiful. I taste the turnip stew and ask where the bathroom is. You say you'll show me. We walk past the table of cackling drunk women reading poems. You take my hand and lead me down the hallway. I spin you around and against the wall. Someone's in the bathroom. I look at your dancing eyes and your beautiful lips and tell you, "You're the hottest fucker I've ever seen." Your eyes light up and your lips smile. We kiss in the hallway. I'm lost when I kiss you. I feel your ass as you wrap your long leg around me. You feel how hard I am and smile, then kiss me again. Running my hand through your hair. Grabbing the back of your head. Pulling you closer. The bathroom flushes and a little old Chinese granny totters out. We go inside and lock the door. You sit on the sink and ask, "How's the turnip stew?" I lift up your skirt and pull down your black thong. Fuck, you're so wet. "It's a tasty turnip stew," I whisper, "you hot fucking turnip." I want to taste you. I spread your legs and kiss your thighs. You taste so sweet. My tongue on your clit. Sliding inside your wet lips. Feeling you gush in my mouth. Hearing you moan as my tongue runs over and back on your swollen clit. Running up and down the side, then licking it again and again. You grab my head as you get close, my tongue deep in your sweet, tight pussy. You grab my hair and moan loud as you cum, pushing your clit into my mouth, me sucking on it and licking your turnip pussy. Jesus, you're fucking hot. Thank God the bathroom is clean and I'm not kneeling on wet patches. I stand up and you grab me to kiss. I can feel your body heat as you reach for my cock and open my pants. You get on your knees and lick from my balls to the tip slowly, kissing the top, then licking again to get my hard cock wet. You look at me while sucking my balls, then run your tongue along the shaft and take it all in your mouth. Jesus Christ, I'm so fucking turned on for you. You have my hard cock dripping wet and bursting to cum. I want to feel you. You stand up and kiss me, then sit on the sink again. I slide inside your dripping pleasure pond, my ponder pipe piping, ready to explode. I can feel your cum on me as you slide up and down my rock hard cock. You're so fucking pretty. I see you biting your lip and grab your ass, shooting hard and cumming deep inside you. I shoot again as we kiss, your beautiful soft lips. Fuck. You're amazing. Malibu is burning. L.A. is raining. Chicago is frozen. But you're so savage. I recommend the turnip stew.

WHITE SWEATER

We're at Target. I'm very hungover and you're doing the hula hoop in an aisle. It's Super Bowl Sunday. I'm so goosed I forgot. Malibu is burning. People keep shooting women. 21 Savage is being deported. It's sad. But you look so delightful in your Sunday best. Your white, old lady sweater and blue jeans and black boots. Sometimes I get confused looking at you. How are you this beautiful and sound and savage and nice and a deviant and delightful and good at hula hooping all at the same time? It makes me ponder. I'll look to the sky and just wonder. Then my ponder pipe will start piping thinking of you. You look at me and laugh "Are you impressed?" You're a hot fucker and an impressive hula hooper. "Yes," I tell you, kissing your beautiful red lips. You feel my pants and smile. "Are you hard already?" you ask me. "Not yet. That's actually a carrot." I needed something to eat and left the house in a hurry and grabbed a carrot by mistake. Maybe I'm still drunk. Better a carrot than the sad persimmon that was in the fridge. Thinking about you and fruit gets me hard. I tell you you're prettier than the sky and your eyes light up. They're unreal. You're a bucket of joy. A true hot turnip fucker. I want to fuck you with the carrot. "Do you want to fuck me with your carrot?" you ask. You can read minds. I take your hand and ask the Target employee where the bathroom is. He points us to the corner. We are going to be late for your sister's party. She has new baby chickens she wants to show you. I try to think of chickens while walking down the aisle. I just can't stop thinking about your eyes. We lock the bathroom door and look at each other. "Hi." "Hello hot fucker." You're so beautiful. Your handsome face. You hate that compliment. I open your jeans and slide them down to your knee high boots. They're not coming off. I kiss your thighs and legs and grab your ass. You smell amazing, like a field of turnips on a cold, summer's day. I love your skin. Why do all my compliments sound like a serial killer's? I slide your white thong down your legs. White for the Lord's day. You're a good girl. I kiss your legs and around your pussy. Your pussy is already wet as I run my tongue along your lips and over your clit. I run it up and down, feeling your clit swell and get bigger. You start to moan softly as I lick up and down your clit and slide my tongue inside your wet pussy. "Oh heck," you say. Fuck, you turn me on so much with your ways. You spread your legs wider but they're trapped in your jeans and boots. I lick your clit and kiss your thighs, sliding a finger inside your warm pussy. "The carrot." you say, between moans. Oh yeah. The carrot. Just like God intended. I slide the carrot inside your tight pussy as my tongue presses against your clit. You're moaning louder and louder as the carrot fucks you and

I slowly lick your throbbing clit. Fuck. I want to bite. Your ass clenches as you cum and press my head into your pussy. I'm so hard for you. "Kiss me," you say. I stand up and kiss your soft lips. Jesus, you're the dream. You take the carrot and bite the top. Sorry, God. You turn around and wiggle your ass at me. You hot fucker. I slide my hard cock inside your wet pussy and fuck you from behind. "Spank me." I spank your right cheek hard. You moan loud and bite your lip. I spank harder and you moan again. "Harder." I spank your perfect ass red and you smile in delight. You're looking at me in the mirror as I fuck you. You raise your head like you want me to choke you. I reach and squeeze your neck. Your eyes close then open and shine. Fuck. You're too hot. I cum hard inside you, shooting deep inside. You keep slapping your ass against me, squeezing every drop. Your pussy is dripping wet against me. You're the most beautiful sky ever. You smile at me, then take another bite of carrot. Malibu is burning. People are being deported. The Rams lost. It's sad. But you're the best hula hooper. And now we get to go meet some chickens. You hot carrot fucker.

GREEN BIKINI

It's Valentine's Day. Malibu is burning. They're building a wall. I think it's going to rain. It's sad. You bought me a new bikini for Valentine's. It's green. Looks Irishish. It's for you. I bought you a new teapot. It's stunning. It's for me. You threw out my last teapot. "That teapot is trash," you told me. Then threw it out. Now I call you my trash teapot. You like it. You are a trash teapot. I'm making tea in the kitchen. It's Thursday. I'm going to hot yoga. You're waltzing around, trying on your bikini for some reason. You come over and kiss me. Trying to distract me from my Irish tea. It doesn't work. "When are you taking me to Paris?" you ask. "You are Paris," I tell you. Your eyes light up. You're a hot fucker. I think I stole that line. But I don't tell you. I'm a creep. You take a sip from my cup. Your lips look beautiful.

I kiss you back and taste how good. You taste like tea. I kiss you harder and you feel me getting hard. Tea always turns me on. Good old Irish tea. I undo your bikini top and let it fall to the ground. You're so fucking beautiful. With your boobs like raindrops. They're amazing. Your body is insane. The hottest. You remind me of the movie Showgirls, my favourite movie in Ireland. And now you're taking my cock out of my pants and kissing it. Running your tongue up and down it slowly, along the side and then the top. Feeling it get harder with your wet lips on my balls. You take a sip of tea, then take my cock in your mouth. Fuck. Feels amazing with the tea. Your hot tea mouth. You swallow the tea and start sucking my hard cock, slowly deep throating it, then back out to kiss and lick the top. I'm so hard for you. Jesus Christ, you're a hot trash teapot. You take my teabag off the counter and rub it on my balls, then lick the tea off them. You suck my balls while pressing the teabag against them. I love you teabagging me. Stroking my cock. On your knees. Looking up at me then taking my cock in your mouth. I want to taste you. You stand up and kiss me. Your soft wet lips. Fuck. You are Paris. I get lost kissing you. I sit you on the counter and kiss your neck, down to your hard nipples. You moan as my tongue glides over them, slowly back and forth, then sucking on them. I kiss your stomach and down to your thighs, pulling off your green bikini thong. Your pussy is soaked, like an Irish field on a wet summer's day. I lick your clit and feel how swollen it is for me. Throbbing. You moan as I lick it again and again, feeling it get bigger. You're pushing your pussy into me as my tongue slides inside your soft lips, my mouth filling with your wetness. You taste so good, like a hot cup of tea on a cold spring day. I take the teabag and rub it along your clit, then slide it inside your warm pussy. I kiss your thigh and take it back out, sliding my tongue inside. Fuck. You have the nicest pussy in Paris. I fuck you with my tongue and lick your swollen clit. I feel you clench your ass as you cum hard in my mouth. "Fuck me." I stand up and kiss you, picking you up. I slide my cock inside and fill your pleasure pond. I fuck you against the wall, kissing your lips, squeezing on your neck. I'm lost in Paris. "Fuck me, famine boy," you say looking at me. I cum hard inside you, shooting deep three times. Fuck. You're amazing. Malibu is burning. They're building a wall. I think it's going to rain. But you are fucking Paris. Sorry, cup of tea.

THE CARROT

It's Sunday. Malibu is burning. The Oscars are on. It's cold. I'm so hungover I can't hear. It's sad. So sad. I can't open this bottle of Pedialyte. It's too hard. I'm sweating in the kitchen. The seal is stuck. I'm eating a carrot to calm down. Carrots always calm me down. You walk in from the bedroom. Wearing a black hoodie, black boots and a red thong. You look fucking hot. Jesus, you're unreal. Now I'm hard and sweating and hungover. "What are you reading?" I ask you. "The Bible," you say. Nice. Catholic guilt. On the Lord's day. "No need to read that," I tell you. I walk over and take it from you. You take my carrot from me and I have a bite. I put the bible on the table as you sit on it. "Like my boots?" I do, you hot fucker. You wrap your legs around me and pull me closer. "Fuck me with your carrot, Father." You're a bad girl. You still want to fuck a priest. I must punish you for such sinful ways. I take the carrot and kiss your lips. Your bottom lip is just hanging and soft and wet and beautiful. And your fucking eyes. Unreal. You're a chancer and a fucker. I like it. They light up as you smile at me. "Fuck me with your carrot," you tell me again. I slide your red thong down your long legs. I like you in just a cropped hoodie and boots. You're beautiful. You close your eyes as I run the carrot along your thighs. Teasing it along your pussy. Running it up your clit. You spreading your legs wider. You're a good girl. I slide the carrot inside you as you moan and look at me. Biting your beautiful lips. Being fucked by a carrot. You're dripping wet all over my hand and the carrot. Feels like I'm back in Ireland. Pulling carrots from the wet ground. Getting ready to feed my horse, Trevor. I miss Trevor. He's a good horse. You're a good girl. You open your mouth and ask to taste. You hot fucker. I pull out the wet carrot and let you taste. You suck and bite it, then kiss me. I want to taste your wet ground. I run my tongue along your clit and between your soft lips. You taste amazing, like a warm bowl of turnips on a cold, wet day. Your clit is so swollen and hot. My tongue running over and back along it. Your pussy pushing in my face. I love feeling you cum for me. I press hard on your clit with my tongue and feel you cumming. Grabbing my head. Moaning loud. Dripping down your legs. Fuck you're beautiful. I stand up and you grab me close. Our wet lips kissing as you take out my rock hard cock carrot. You slide me inside you, then wrap your legs around and push me deeper. Filling up your tight wet pussy. You're so warm, I'm so hard inside you. Feeling your nipples under your hoodie. Grabbing your hair. Running my hand over your neck. Squeezing on it. "Fuck me, Father," you tell me. I choke you more. You're a good girl. I get lost fucking you. Your pussy feels so fucking good. You're the hottest woman in the world. I bend you over the table and fuck you from behind. "Spank me," you say. I spank your sexy ass. It's the hottest ass ever. I spank again. "Harder." I spank hard and you moan loud. I pick up the Bible and spank you with it. Sorry, God. Say hi to Trevor. You laugh and spin around. I'm going to cum so hard. You get on your knees and open your mouth. Stroking and sucking as I cum in your mouth. Jesus Christ, feels amazing. Malibu is burning. I miss Trevor. I can't open the Pedialyte. But fuck me, you're just the hottest fucker ever.

WHITE ON WHITE

It's Sunday. The Lord's day. I'm just getting back from shows on the road. You've been away for a month with work. Malibu is burning. J-Lo got engaged. We missed International Women's Day. R Kelly is going mental. It's sad. So sad. But I get to see you again. You hot fucker. I walk in and you're leaning in the kitchen doorway. You're dressed in a white sweater, white thong and white Nike. Your casual Sunday outfit. You look so fucking beautiful. I haven't even put my bags down and you have me hard. "Hello, hot fucker." I tell you. "Hi, fucker," you reply. "Why do you look sad?" I ask. "I haven't been fucked in a month." Jesus, you're so sexy. I walk over and kiss your beautiful lips. They're so soft and wet, I fucking love them. I pull back and look in your eyes. Sweet Jesus, your face, it's so fucking pretty. "Want some apple?" you ask me. "Yes please." You hand me a slice from your plate on the counter. I bite it and you eat half. I pull you close as we kiss again, you rubbing my hard cock through my jeans, me grabbing your perfect ass. I lift you up onto the counter and slide your white thong down your long legs. Your Nike come off too. I spread your legs and pull you closer. I want to taste you. I want to taste an apple in you. I take a slice and slide it inside your wet pussy. You smile at me while I'm doing it, moaning as it slides inside. "Did you go to Mass today?" you ask. "I didn't. Did you?" "Yes. I'm a good Catholic girl." Yeah you are. You're a good girl. I squeeze your neck, looking at your eyes and lips, as you unzip my jeans and take out my hard cock. You run your finger over the precum and taste it. I squeeze your neck harder as you close your eyes and stroke my cock. I kiss your lips and neck, sliding your sweatshirt over your head. Fuck, your body is amazing. The hottest fucking body I've ever seen. I kiss your neck and boobs, running my tongue over your hard nipples, kissing slowly and sucking, hearing you moan. You push my head lower, my tongue and lips on your stomach and sexy thighs. Your skin is so soft and sweet. I spread your legs and kiss along the top of your pussy, teasing my tongue lightly on your clit and along your lips. I want to taste your apple pussy. I run my tongue between your wet lips and the apple slice slides out. I take it in my mouth and have you taste it too. Your apple pussy tastes so fucking good. I feed you the apple and your wet lips take it in. Reminds me of feeding my cow back home in Ireland, Daisy. She was a great cow, always so nice. You're so nice too. You're a good girl. I want you to cum. I lick your wet pussy again, running my tongue over your clit, up and down slowly, harder, feeling you get wetter. You're as wet as a muddy field on a rainy summer's day. I miss

Daisy. She's a good girl. Your wet pussy is running down your thighs. Dripping to your ass. I run my tongue down and taste. You moan louder as my tongue slides inside. You're fucking wet all over. I slowly slide a finger in your ass as my tongue slides into your wet pussy. Your ass is clenching. I want you to cum. I take an apple slice and slide it in your ass. "Oh fuck," you moan. Your pussy pushing in my face. My tongue buried deep. Rubbing your clit. Feeling your ass shake. You moaning loud as you cum for me. You're a good girl. Cumming in my mouth. You're so fucking wet. I want to feel my hard cock inside your wet muddy field. I stand up and pull you to me on the counter. Your legs wrap around and my cock slides deep inside. You're so warm and wet and tight. You feel fucking amazing. I'm kissing your wet lips and choking your neck as you're grabbing my ass and back, making me fuck you deeper. "I'm going to cum again," you say out loud. Cum for me, you hot fucker. Your body clenches as you grab me tight. I choke you tighter as you cum harder. You kiss me hard and gasp for air. You jump off the counter and flip around, grabbing my cock and sliding it inside from behind. Your ass slapping off my thighs, your wet pussy cumming on my hard cock still, looking back at me over your shoulder, my hand tight on your neck. You're a good Catholic girl. Fuck. I'm cumming with you. I shoot hard inside you, so fucking deep. I stay hard and you keep slapping your ass back on me, fucking the cum out of me. I cum hard again and choke you harder. Fuck. I pull out and you spin around. You want to taste my cum. You stroke and suck my wet hard cock, making me cum again inside your mouth. Fuck, you have a wetter mouth than Daisy. You feel fucking amazing. Malibu is burning. I missed IWD. J-Lo is married. It's sad. So sad. But you're the hottest fucker. I need some cold brew. And there's a slice of apple in your ass, you hot, lovely cow.

BLACK PENCIL SKIRT

It's Monday. I've a five day hangover. So goosed. I'm meeting you for lunch. My poor head is pounding. You just got back from New York. It was too cold. Malibu is burning. Conor McGregor just got arrested. It's sad. So sad. But I'm hungry. And horny. I've been wanting to kiss your lips for so long. All weekend. You beauty. I get to your office and your assistant Greg waves me in. Greg hates me. He just likes you too. He reminds me of my cousin's pet pigeon when we were young. Fuck you, Greg. Fuck you, pigeons. I knock on the door as I open it. Classic dumb move. You look up and smile. Fucking Christ. You look fucking amazing. Grey turtleneck. Black pencil skirt. Black heels. Are you trying to kill me? With your hair tied up. Your black rimmed glasses. And your lips looking so fucking juicy with your red lipstick. It just annoyed me how hot you are. No wonder Instagram bans women showing nipples. Men are dumb. We go crazy for beautiful nipples. You're a human beautiful nipple. You drive me insane how beautiful you are. Fuck. Jesus. Fuck you Greg. "I got a new iPhone," you tell me. Struggling to figure it out. "I hear the vibration is strong on them," I tell you. You look at me and smile with your deviant delightful eyes. You're the hottest demon I know. I eat some grapes that are on your desk. "You look unreal," I tell you. "Oh yeah?" Oh yeah, fucker. "Are you hard?" you ask, looking at my pants. "Yeah, fully. I'm annoyed. You're too hot." "Well sorry about that." "Not good enough." I tell you. "Are you going to punish me?" you ask, putting down the phone and looking at me with your fuck eyes. Fuck, you're even hotter at your office. You're the fucking boss. "I want to fuck you and feel you cum on your desk." You look at me and bite your lip. "Can you lock the door?" No, I tell you. If Greg walks in he can watch you cumming. "Now get on your hands and knees on the desk." You do as you're told. You're a good girl. You're so fucking sexy. Like a little pony on the desk. Waiting for me to tell you what to do. Who's my little pony? Fuck you, Greg. "Don't move." I tell you. I pull your skirt up. Your ass is perfect. Fuck. It's the nicest I've seen. I like that you're wearing the tiniest of black thongs. I pull it down your legs, you lifting a knee one at a time to slide it off. I rub a cheek, then the other. I start to slowly kiss the back of your thighs. Down to the back of your knees, then slowly up again, kissing your ass cheeks and teasing your ass and pussy. Kissing around your ass. Kissing along the outside of your wet pussy. Hearing you moan as my mouth pauses over your clit. Blowing on it. Feeling it get hotter for me. Feeling it get bigger for me. Feeling it get swollen as my tongue lightly licks it. Slowly up and down. Feeling it swell even more as my tongue teases and runs over and back. Hearing you moan as my tongue tastes how wet you are. I take three grapes and slide them inside your wet pussy. I lick your clit again slowly. I like how big it gets when you're really turned on. You're the hottest fucker. You're moaning and breathing deep and hard as my tongue plays with your ass. Teasing and licking. Fingers rubbing your clit. I slide my tongue inside then run it down to your clit again. Your ass is shaking. You love me licking your clit. Your pussy is dripping wet for me. You're a good girl. I take your new phone and hold it against your clit. I hope it's water resistant. Your pussy is drenched. As I phone your phone it vibrates on your clit. You start moaning so loud, saying "oh fuck" over and over. A grape pops out as the phone vibrates over and over. Tastes unreal. The sweetest wine. You have the sweetest pussy. I slide my tongue inside as the phone vibrates on your clit. "I'm cumming baby," you tell me, arms shaking and legs trembling. You cum hard in my mouth as I lick your pussy from behind. You're face down on the desk cumming in my mouth, grapes popping everywhere, your new phone dripping wet. "Turn over." I tell you. You're panting on your desk. You collapse face down then flip around. Looking at me with your beautiful lips. "Kiss me." you say. I climb on the desk on top of you. I love dominating you. You're the hottest fucker alive. I kiss your soft lips slowly. Your neck. Your ear. Back to your lips. I'm so fucking hard for you. My cock out of my jeans. Rubbing along your swollen clit. Getting it bigger and harder. Your pussy soaking my balls. "Am I a good girl?" you ask. "You're a good girl." I tell you, as you slide my rock hard cock inside your perfect pussy. It's so loud and wet as my cock slides in and out of your wet warm mud patch. We're like two horny ponies. Fuck. You feel fucking amazing. You look so hot in your turtleneck. We both look good in our turtlenecks fucking. "Fuck me, Father" you whisper in my ear. You really do have a priest fetish. You're a bad girl. I squeeze your neck as you close your eyes, my cock deep inside, you sucking on my fingers, lost in our hot fucking. I choke you harder as I feel your pussy tighten on my cock. You're going to cum again. I cover your mouth as you cum hard, your back arching off the table, your legs wrapping and squeezing around me. "Harder," you moan. You're so fucking sexy. I spank your ass and cover your mouth. You look me in the eyes and your eyes light up with demon delight. Fuck. I'm cumming now too. I shoot hard inside you, fuck you. I shoot again as your body tenses and cum again. Jesus Christ. I'm lost. In you. Unreal. I pull out and cum again. On your phone by mistake. You need another new phone. There's a knock on the door as Greg asks, "Everything OK in there?" Fuck off, Greg. I climb off the desk and stand there, gathering my bearings. You get off and drop to your knees, sucking and licking the cum off my cock. You're so fucking sexy. Malibu is burning. McGregor was arrested. You want to fuck priests. I'm so hungry. But that was hot. You're the hottest boss ever. Thanks, you fucking boss.

WHITE HOODIE

I'm at home eating some porridge. It's been a long week. Thank God for porridge. Malibu is burning. Friends are fighting. There's some college admissions scandal. And the Earth is dying. But at least we have porridge. And I have you. Thanks, God. I missed three FaceTimes from you. I've given up accepting them for Lent. You gave up chocolate. Your weakness. You boss woman. Just as I'm finishing my bowl you walk in. Back from the gym. Jesus, you look unreal. I can't go to the gym with you anymore. I get too turned on. You're a demon. You turn me into a deviant. It's the best. You're wearing your white, crop top hoodie, tight black gym pants, black Nike and your black hat back to front. Fucking Christ. You look like the dream. You walk in, see me and stop. "What's up?" "Hi." You look flustered. Your beautiful cheeks go red. Your golden eyes smile. You've been caught. "What are you doing?" I ask. "I didn't think you'd be home," you tell me, hiding something. You have chocolate. "Show me the chocolate." "It's not chocolate," you say, laughing. "Show me." You laugh and pout and pull the out the chocolate from behind your back. You're a bad girl. "I'm sorry, Father," you say, head down. "Time to punish you," I say. I don't care about the chocolate. You just like being punished. You like being a bad good girl. "What are you going to do?" you ask me. "Go to the bed," I tell you, "Be lying face down, naked, waiting for me." You look at me and your eyes light up. You like being punished. I'm going to make your ass red raw. I go to the kitchen while you go to the bedroom. Get a lighter and a wooden spoon. You love the wooden spoon. It's what parents spank children with in Ireland when they're bold and bad. You're a bad, bold girl. You must be spanked. I walk into the bedroom and you're naked on the bed, on your hands and knees, ass in the air. You already know what's going to happen. Your handcuffs are already on your back. I walk over and rub your perfect ass. It's like an apple mango peach. It looks so fucking good and tasty. I massage it then spank you really hard. The loud smack makes you clench and moan. "What was that for?" "I told you to be lying face down, not on your hands and knees." I spank you hard again as you moan loud then bite your lip, breathing hard. That made you wet. "I'm sorry," you say, lying down like a good girl. I rub your right cheek and spank it hard twice, making your body tense with pleasure. Now both cheeks are red. I take your handcuffs and cuff your hands to the bed. I take two scarves and tie your feet to the bottom of the bed. You're spread out. Can't move. Face down. I can see a smile on your beautiful face. You're so pretty. I spank again and you moan and smile, biting your juicy bottom lip to hide it. "Are you going to be a good girl?" I ask you, opening the chocolate and starting to melt it with the lighter. I watch it drip onto your lower back as you clench with each drop. I spank you hard with the wooden spoon on each cheek. Your ass is so red. You won't be able to sit down. Reminds me of when the nuns would beat us in Ireland. They'd just use their fists. Sister Mary O'Rourke. She's dead now. Such a horny nun. Loved a dirty pun. I spank you again and taste the chocolate on your back. You taste so sweet. Your pussy is glistening and dripping already. You're so wet. Good girl. I put the lighter to the back of the wooden spoon then spank you hard again. Your ass looks like a red apple and peach. Your pussy looks like a sweet mango between it. I want to taste your pleasure pond. See if it's like a wet whistle on a soaking Irish spring day. You're a wet whistle. I slide a finger inside your wet whistling pussy. Fuck. You're soaked. I slide two in as I lick your clit from behind. It's swollen and big already. Your pussy feels so tight and wet. You're so turned on you bad girl. I spank you both cheeks again and you moan and bite the pillow. I finger your whittling wet whistle while licking your throbbing click. You're squirming on the bed tied up. "Don't stop," you tell me. I spank you with the spoon hard, then tease you with the other end. You love being spoon fucked. I lick your clit and flick it with my tongue. I gently bite your left ass cheek, then kiss and bite the other. You love it. Your ass grinds up and down as your pussy begs for me. I'm finger fucking you and licking your hot clit, teasing, knowing you're close to cumming. I slide the spoon inside and you moan hard. Your hands and feet clench and tighten on the bed as the spoon fucks you deep. You're moaning and screaming into the pillow. You love being fucked by a fucking spoon. Your legs shake as I press on your clit. You're going to cum hard. You moan, "Oh fuck baby," as you start to cum so hard. You're soaked. I rub your clit as you're cumming and you start squirting hard. Fuck. That's so hot. You're wet mango squirting on me. You hot fucker. Jesus, you came so hard and so much. The bed is soaked. Bad girl. You bite the pillow and push your pussy and ass back. You want my hard cock. I'm like a rock. It's so big sliding inside your soaking pussy. I fuck you deep, my body dominating yours on the bed. I spank your red ass and grab you by the back of the neck. Below your hair. Pushing you down as my cock goes deeper. Fuck, you have me so turned on. It's like I'm fucking a waterfall. I must take you to one in Ireland. You love nature and shrubbery. You're a good shrub. I bite your shoulder as my cock feels your pussy tighten. Jesus Christ. I'm lost in you. I squeeze your neck from behind and spank your ass more. I start rubbing your clit as I'm fucking you. You start squirting again on me. Fucking Jesus. I was just trying to enjoy me porridge. Your ass and pussy tighten and I start to cum hard deep inside you. Fucking Christ. I shoot twice as we keep fucking. You're wetter than a cup of tea. Your back is glistening. Golden sweat. I pull out and cum on the chocolate. Sorry, chocolate. You lay there breathing hard while I'm kneeling behind you. You look around and see the chocolate, then flop your head down and smile. You open your mouth. I feed you the chocolate like a good girl. Malibu is burning. The Earth is dying. We fucked up Lent. It's sad. But you're my apple mango peach. And a hot fucking shrub with the wettest fucking whistle. Thanks, spoon.

BLACK KNEE HIGH

We're in Ireland. It's St. Patrick's Day. Malibu is burning. Here it's raining. We're at a funeral. My great Aunt Nelly passed away. It's sad. So sad. I never met her but she was a great woman. Used to send me money every birthday. Four shillings and a leaf of clover. I'd always eat the clover, for luck. Cork is cold. The church is cold. You're looking ridiculously hot though. Black dress. Black knee high socks. Black boots. You're the sexiest mourner I've seen. It's your first time in Ireland. You're too pretty for the island. It's insane. I've never been so turned on at a funeral. Tucking up my boner every time you touch my hand or I smell your hair. I usually get turned on at funerals for some reason but this is too much. Maybe it's the suit pants. Too tight. Too hard. Too much. The priest gave a lovely sermon, Father

O'Shaughnessy. We all wept. He's a horny man though. Kept massaging my shoulders while I drank wine from the goblet. I think you got jealous. "Come," I whisper to you, while people are kneeling and praying, waiting for communion to finish. Your solemn eyes light up. You take my hand and follow me out the side door. It's so grey outside. Raining. Obviously. So wet. Always. My poor hair. "I'm so horny," you say in a hushed voice. "Me too," I tell you, as you reach for my hard cock. Ready to burst through my suit pants. I take you around the back of the church. It's quiet. Not as windy. It's very wet and muddy though, like a wet field back here. I lost my virginity here. In the mud, while it was raining. First time was when I fucked a can of corned beef. Irish tradition we do on Paddy's Day. It's how St. Patrick stayed faithful to God and didn't stray. Fucking beef. Second time was with a girl. She almost felt as good as the beef. I slipped in mud. While wearing white jeans. It was great. We never spoke again. "What are you thinking about?" you ask, while on your knees, unzipping my pants. "Corned beef," I moan, as you take my hard cock in your wet mouth. Fuck. You're like a plunge pool. You run your tongue along the top of my cock, then slowly down the shaft to my balls. Sucking my balls with your wet lips while stroking my hard cock. Jesus. You're so hot. Never got a blowjob in Ireland. I think they're banned. You're a bad girl. Kneeling in mud, sucking and stroking my cock. Behind a church. Such a bad girl. You need to be spanked. You're looking at me in the eye as you run your tongue up and down my bulging cock. You have me so fucking turned on. Watching you rub your pussy as you swallow my cock. Sliding it deep down your throat. Slowly taking it out. Rubbing it on your lips. Slapping your face with my cock. Covering your lips with precum and your drool all over my cock. I pull your hair behind your head and fuck your mouth, slowly then faster. Fucking Christ. You're even better than beef. I want to fill you up. I pull my cock out of your mouth and you look at me smiling. Next to you I see a ruler on the ground, "where did you get that?" "I stole it from the pew next to me." You're a bad fucking girl. I'm going to spank you with it. "Crawl to the wall," I tell you. You're on your hands and knees in mud.

But you do as you're told. You crawl towards the wall and wait for me. Your perfect ass in the air. Cold and horny. Dress pulled up. Like a good girl. I take the ruler and rub your ass cheek, then smack hard on the right side. It's a loud crack. You flinch and moan. You're a bad girl. I smack again and you moan harder. Your ass is red. I like it. You love it. I smack again with the ruler as you moan and almost buckle. Your ass grinds up and down in pain and pleasure. You want me inside you. I smack your left cheek until it's as red. You look over your shoulder at me, biting your lip. You're so fucking sexy. "Rub your clit for me," I tell you. You start rubbing it as I spank your ass with my hand. One spank, then the ruler again. You're moaning harder and harder. Clit getting bigger and bigger for me. Pussy getting wetter and wetter. It's glistening from behind. The wind is whistling. Rain is falling. And your ass is so red you won't be able to sit down. "Fuck me," you moan at me. "Say please," I tell you. "Please fuck me," you say again. You're a good girl. I get on my knees in the mud. My suit is ruined. This is how I fucked the can of corned beef too. I think Father O'Shaughnessy saw me doing it. Hopefully he's not watching now. I rub my hard cock off your wet pussy. It's so beautiful. Your sweet mango pussy. I slide inside and fill you up. Fuck me, you feel amazing, like a warm bowl of porridge on a cold Christmas morn. I fuck you from behind, slapping your red ass. My cock deep inside you. You rubbing your clit and dripping wet down your legs. You're so fucking sexy. Your ass and thighs slapping against me. Grabbing your neck. Pulling on your hair. Choking your throat. Feeling your pussy get wetter and tighter on my cock. I rub your ass and spank as you rub your clit. I feel you breathing deep and ass shaking. You're close. I choke you harder and fuck you deeper. My cock deep inside as you start to cum hard. You're moaning and crying out for more. I cover your mouth as you cum and fuck my cock harder. We're like two pigs in muck. I push you face down and fuck you even deeper. You're grinding back on my cock and your pussy is squeezing tighter. Fuck. I think of the beef and start to cum hard, shooting deep inside you. I cum hard again and spank you hard. Jesus Christ. I flip you over so I can kiss your wet lips. You're covered in muck too and look so fucking beautiful. I kiss you as we keep fucking. You still have me rock hard. You open your mouth and look at me. "Let me taste it." I pull my cock out and cum again in your plunge pool. You swallow and smile. We kiss in the muck. Malibu is burning. We are mud pigs. Father O'Shaughnessy was watching us out the window. Aunt Nelly is gone. It's sad. So sad. But fuck that was unreal. You're the hottest. You beautiful beef.

BLACK SNOW PUSSY

We're in Aspen. It's freezing. Malibu is burning. Mueller just released his report. It's sad. So sad. But this hotel is slick. You told me you wanted to give me some snow pussy. I'm always down for snow pussy. The first time we came I was being a bitch. The place was so expensive. And you had just booked a big deal. But we still went half. I stopped being a bitch though. You riding my cock while telling me how much money you just made that day made me so hard. I love Aspen. I love snow pussy. It's freezing outside and you're hungry. You're in your black thong and black bra. You look hot as fuck. Ordering food on the phone. "I'll have the clam chowder and Caesar salad" you tell them. I already ate. Porridge. It was savage. "45 minutes for clam chowder and Caesar salad? Alright. Cool. I guess." You hang up and don't look happy. "That's too long," you tell me. "I know." I say. "I'm going to have to fuck you stupid so I forget I'm hungry," you tell me. "Please do." I'm in my boxers sitting on a chair by the desk in the room. "Don't move," you tell me. Grabbing your handcuffs and scarves. Tying my feet to the chair legs. Handcuffing one hand to the back of the chair. I'm not going anywhere. You kiss my lips and neck, then grab my hair. You're always a bossy fucker when you're by the snow. I like it. You undo your bra as you sit on my lap. Pushing your hard nipple into my face as I kiss and lick, getting it harder as you grind your ass and pussy on my lap. My cock getting harder and harder as I feel your pussy get wet through your thong. You pull my head back again, your dangerous devil eyes looking at me. You like being in control for a change. You stand up and slide your thong down. "You got me wet," you say, almost annoyed. "You have me hard." You turn around and bend over to take your thong off. Your sexy ass and wet pussy teasing me. My cock getting harder and dying to be inside you. You lay on the bed looking at me. You're a hot fucking turnip. You look like a striptease. You start rubbing your body while lying on the bed, looking at me with your devil eyes and weapon body. Touching your nipples and running your hand between your legs. Rubbing your clit slowly. "Touch yourself," you tell me. I do as I'm told. Stroking my cock with my one free hand while you finger your wet pussy. Your stomach breathing deeper up and down as you slide two fingers in. Hearing how wet you are gets me so fucking turned on. I can see your ass grinding on the bed as you finger your wet tight pussy. You have the finest snow pussy of all time. Dripping like a bucket of ice on an Irish summer, a Thursday in June. I'm so fucking turned on. Watching you drip down your legs, thinking about ice cream, dying to fuck your snow pussy. "Fuck, you're so beautiful," I tell you while stroking. You have me so raring to go. "You like that?" you ask. I do. You hot fucker. You arch your back and rub your clit. Two fingers inside. Clit swollen. Pussy dripping. Ready to cum. Your ass clenches and you moan loud as you start to cum on the bed. Fuck. I want to taste. "Sit on my cock," I tell you. You're lying on the bed, tasting your wet fingers, looking at me. You stand up and walk over to me, slapping my face, "Don't tell me what to do." You're a hot fucker. You handcuff my other hand to the chair and pull my boxers off. I'm all yours. Whatever you want. You kiss my lips and body, rubbing your boobs on my cock. Sliding it between your sexy breasts, spitting on it while looking at me in the eye. You start to stroke it while kissing and licking my balls, looking at me the entire time. You're so fucking sexy. "It's hard, huh?" you ask. Yeah it's the hardest. Ready to explode. "You're not allowed to cum yet," you tell me. "Okay." You stand up and turn around. Rubbing my cock along your wet pussy. Fuck. It feels so fucking good. "I'm close to cumming," I tell you. "No." You look at me annoyed. You walk to the villa balcony door and open it. A gust of freezing air rushes in. You bend down and pick up some snow, then walk back over to me. You sit on my lap and put the snow on my chest. "Be a good boy," you tell me. Fucking Jesus Christ. It's so fucking cold. You're so fucking hot. You stand up and turn around again, grabbing my rock hard cock with your freezing hand. "Now fuck my snow pussy," you tell me. You slide me inside you and grind up and down. Your pussy dominating my cock. Arching your back and looking over your shoulder. My body caught in heaven and freezing hell. Your pussy getting wetter and wetter as my cock gets harder and harder. You rubbing your swollen clit. Bouncing on my lap. Ass and back arching and grinding. You start cumming on my cock, hard. Grabbing the arms of the chair as your body clenches and grips then releases. Fuck. You're beautiful. Your sexy back pressed against me. "Cum for me," you tell me. Grinding your soaked pussy on me. Making me think of a 99 ice cream dripping down my hand. Ass slapping on my thighs. I start to cum hard and almost break the chair legs. Shooting deep inside you. Wanting to touch you but all tied up. Jesus fucking Christ. I shoot again inside. Pure joy. You get off and go on your knees. Sucking my cock and tasting the cum. Swallowing as I shoot hard again. Fucking hell. There's a knock at the door. Malibu is burning. Her emails. It's freezing. So sad. But the clam chowder is early. And fuck me, you're the hottest snow pussy.

ORANGE CRAWFISH SWEATER

It's Saturday. We're at a crawfish boil party. I don't know what it is. Malibu is burning. Apparently there was no Russian collusion. It looks like it's going to rain. It's sad. So sad. But I'm boozing. And it's daytime. And we are about to eat. We're at your friend's place in Silverlake. Apparently crawfish boils are a tradition. You just boil a load of fish and corn and sausages and potatoes and eat and eat until they're all gone. While boozing. Sounds like a dream. Glad you insisted on potatoes for Ireland. You're a hot fucking poppy. In your orange sweater, black jeans and black boots. I showed up late. I'm always late. You're two drinks deep and horny. I can tell. Sucking on your straw. Biting your lips. You're a hot fucker. You feed me some crawfish. Looks like a cockroach. "They're the roach of the sea," you tell me, shoving another one in my mouth. They taste tasty. You leave your finger in my mouth for an extra second. There are kids around somewhere in the back yard. But none by us. "What's this?" I ask. "Crab leg. You never tried that?" I'm a simple man. I never tried. You crack open a leg and feed some to me. Fucking hell, this is the juiciest fish ever. "Is this healthy?" I ask like an idiot. "The healthiest. Suck it down." I eat two legs while you suck on some corn. I like watching you eat. Makes me want to unzip your jeans and eat your wet crawfish pussy. I can tell you're horny because you come up and whisper in my ear, "I'm so fucking horny." Apparently crab makes me horny too because now I'm hard. Cock pressing against my jeans. I want your body on me. "Let's fuck," you whisper to me. "Where?" "Meet me at the bottom of the garden, there's a little recording studio there." You finish your drink and go first. I finish up some more fish and potatoes and watch you leave. Fuck, your ass is so juicy, like a bowl of gravy drenched potatoes. While I'm watching you, a kid appears out of nowhere next to me. Just staring at me. He keeps staring so I ask him his name. He looks at me then walks away crying. Fuck. For some reason I feel like a pedophile. Nice. No clue why. I finish more fish then follow you down the garden through the bushes. Away from wailing kids. I think his name is Terry. His Dad is Terry Senior. It's his house I think. Why name your kid Terry? I should phone child services. I get to the little recording studio shed and open the wooden door. You're standing by a couch, just wearing your orange sweater and black boots. "Where are your pants?" "They came off, whoops." Oh you're boozed up. I like it. I want to kiss your wet lips. I pull you close to me and kiss you slowly. Fuck.

Your ass in my hands, your wet thong pushing into my hard cock. My jeans need to come off too. You unzip them and slide them down. You sit on the couch and kiss my thighs, slowly to my balls then spit on my cock. I'm breathing deep as you stroke my hard cock, spitting and licking. I look down as you look up at me smiling. You tie your hair in a ponytail and start sucking my cock. I love you sucking me after a couple of drinks, your mouth is even wetter and you're even hornier. Spit dripping down my balls as you deep throat me, gagging on my cock then pulling it out and stroking again. Fuck. I love looking at your eyes as you suck on my balls. I want to taste how wet you are. I lie you back on the couch and kiss your wet thong. It's soaked. You horny potato. I pull at it with my teeth then slide it down your legs, over your boots. You spread your legs for me and arch your back as you lie fully on the couch. Moaning and closing your eyes as my lips kiss your thighs, slowly, until my tongue is running up and down the outside of your pussy. You're so fucking wet as I slide inside your pleasure pond, my tongue tasting how sweet you are. You gush as my tongue slides in and out, then slowly licking your clit. I can feel it getting bigger and throbbing as I start to suck on it. You press my head in so I suck on it more. Your ass is clenching and gyrating on the couch as I finger your tight pussy and suck your swollen clit. I can feel you close to cumming. Breathing deep. Moaning softly. Legs starting to tremble. I want to taste your crawfish pussy cumming for me. I press my tongue against your clit and finger you as you cum in my mouth. You're a good girl. Keep cumming for me. You press my head then pull me up to kiss you. I kiss your wet lips and let you taste your pussy. You hot fucker. You take my cock and slide it inside you. Jesus Christ, I'm lost in how hot and wet you are. Feels like I'm in Ireland running through a field of wet mud, pure bliss and heaven. Your pussy is so fucking wet, like Father O'Rourke's hair when he would show up for Mass just out of the shower. Still dripping on his shoulders. Your pussy dripping down my balls. You pushing me deeper inside. My hand on your neck. Squeezing the sides. Watching you bite your lip. Spitting in your mouth. Slapping that ass. Fucking you slow.

Your ass grinding. Going quicker. Your eyes and mouth opening wide then closing as you cum again. I feel your pussy tighten and cum with you. Shooting hard deep inside you. Fucking you deeper as I cum again. Kissing you hard and wet as I stay hard and we keep fucking. I pull out and cum on your boobs. You love it. Biting your lip and rubbing a finger in the cum. Sucking on it. Lying there happy and smiling. You're a hot fucker. You wipe off the cum with your panties then throw them in the rubbish bin. "Terry Senior can keep them as a souvenir." Malibu is burning. No collusion. Terry Junior's mother is asking people at the party who made her son cry. It's sad. But you're hottest crawfish ever. You hot crawfish fucker.

YELLOW BEANIE

We're in New York. It's cold. Malibu is burning. I lost my headphones. So sad. So cold. So sad. I just got out of the shower. You had me so turned on all day while walking around. Telling me how wet you were. Sliding my hand down your pants to feel. You have the nicest, wettest pussy. I had to leave for a meeting. You went to get a tattoo. I walk out of the bathroom in the hotel room. You're back. Lying on the bed. Naked but in a blue thong and a yellow beanie. "I'm hot. But cold. But hot," you tell me. Fair enough. I love your blue thong. Maybe I just love it on you. But your ass always looks amazing in it. Now I'm fucking hard again. Towel around my waist, wrestling to hide my boner. You have the perfect body. Your sexy stomach. Your beautiful boobs. Your long legs. Jesus. You're a hot fucker. "What are you eating?" I ask. "Some sort of tart," you tell me. You're a tart. "And ice cream." I want to eat you. "Do you want to eat me?" you ask, reading my mind. "I do." "Well then come eat me." You turn over and lie face down on the bed, ass in the air, looking over your shoulder at me. My towel comes off, you have my cock rock hard. I get on the bed behind you, running my hands along your legs. I see your new tattoo on your arm, a turnip with a stem. You're a hot turnip. I like it a lot. "Give me the ice cream," I tell you while massaging your ass. You hand it to me like a good girl. My hard cock is teasing your ass and wet pussy, sliding between your ass cheeks, my hands pressing on your lower back. You arch your back and try to make me slide inside you. Not yet, fucker. I kiss your back and massage your shoulders, my cock teasing your wet pussy and tight ass. I massage your neck as you close your eyes and moan. My hands around your neck, squeezing lightly as my hard cock is sliding between your cheeks. I'm so fucking turned on and you're so fucking wet. I take the tub of ice cream and scoop out a spoonful, then flop it on your ass. Your cheeks clench as the cold hits it, then relaxes again. Thank God you got vanilla and not chocolate fudge. "Eat my ass," you say moaning and frustrated. I will. I hope it's gluten free. I taste the ice cream on your asshole. Seems gluten free. I lick your ass and slide a tongue inside. You moan and bury your head in the pillow. My tongue sliding inside your sexy tight ass, my fingers rubbing your wet pussy and clit. I feel your clit get bigger as I slowly press over and back, tongue and ice cream filling your ass. You love it being eaten. I take another spoon of ice cream and flop it down. You moan louder as your ass clenches and relaxes. I bury my tongue inside you again. You taste so good. Reminds me of the ice cream I had growing up every rain day in Ireland. We would eat ice cream in the rain. Nelly at the corner shop would sell it to us, the old lady who owned the post office too. She's dead now. So sad. Fat Frogs were my favourite ice cream. Back then at least. Now it's eating ice cream from your hot fucking turnip ass. Your pussy is fucking drenched for me. Dripping on my hand and the bed. My tongue fucking your ass. You moaning louder and louder. You're so wet. I want to see you squirt. You start to cum as I rub your swollen throbbing clit and eat your ass from behind. "Squirt for me," I tell you. You turn over onto your back and starting rubbing your clit while I finger you. Two fingers inside your soaking pleasure pond. Watching you bite your lip, back arching, as I finger you to cum again. Your ass lifts off the bed as you rub your clit faster. You start moaning loud and cumming hard again, ass shaking and legs quivering as you squirt and cum. Fuck, it's so fucking sexy. I love you squirting. "Fucking kiss me," you tell me. I climb on top and kiss your beautiful soft lips. You push my ass into you and slide my hard cock inside. Jesus Christ, you feel amazing. Like my cock just entered heaven. Feels even better than that time when I was young and fell in mud and started pumping the warm, wet mud. Puddle Pumper Hayes they called me. Nelly watched me do it too. I'm dominating your sexy body. Feels like I'm close to cumming already. You're sucking my fingers as I'm squeezing your neck. Fuck, you're a good girl. You look me in the eyes while sucking and I feel your pussy tighten on my cock. I cum hard inside you, shooting deep. You open your mouth and I spit inside. Oh you wanted my cum. I fuck you slowly knowing I'm going to shoot again. I take out my cock and you start to suck just as I start cumming again. Fucking Christ. You are heaven. It's cold. Malibu is burning. I need new headphones. It's sad. But that was fucking hot. You fat frog fucking delight.

HOT NEON THONG

I get back from the gym absolutely goosed. Malibu is burning. You were gone for two weeks. I did two hot a hot yoga class. It's sad. So sad. But now you're back. A photo shoot in Thailand. Hanging with some ladyboys. I walk into the apartment and you're in the kitchen. Wearing just a neon yellow thong. Jesus Christ, your ass is the finest ass I'll ever see. It's like a bubble of joy and delight. Your thong tight on you. Your tan looks so good. Brown back and legs. I'm standing in the doorway just admiring your beauty. Realising I'm already hard. For fuck's sake. You turn around as you hear the door closing. You're playing with a neon yo-yo. My gift from Thailand. That thong is my gift really. Jesus. You're unreal. You deserve books written about you. You fine fucker. "What are you making?" "Cajun chicken." I see your coy smile. You're boozing. Trying to beat jet lag. An old Irish trick. Keep boozing until you sleep for 12 hours. Classic. I want to kiss your boozing lips. You sit on the sink and place your hand between your legs. "Come here," you tell me. I walk over as you take a swig of vodka. You wrap your legs around my waist and arms around my neck. You kiss me hard, putting booze in my mouth. Your wet tongue dancing with mine. Your lips dripping on mine. You pull back and hand me some pickle juice. "Take a swig," you tell me. Swig on. I take a drink from the vodka bottle and kiss you this time. Hands on your back and ass as you take vodka from me. Your perfect boobs pressed against me. Vodka running down our mouths. We take more pickle juice and go again. Each time we kiss we get hornier and hornier. My hands running through your hair. You grabbing mine. Pulling you close. Pulling at your thong. You stop me touching your pussy and push me back. You keep me at leg's length. "Take off my neon thong," you tell me. I slide it down your legs as you take another swig. Swig on. You hand me the bottle as your hand covers your pussy. I fucking want you so bad. You know it. Bad girl. You let booze drip from your mouth down your beautiful body. Jesus Christ you're a heaven. Your brown body driving my porridge white body mental. "Take off your clothes," you tell me. I rip my t-shirt off and pull my shorts down. You bite your bottom lip as my hard cock flops out, standing there like a lone soldier, or a priest waiting in the church garden for directions from God. "Stroke it," you tell me. I start stroking while you rub your hard nipples and breasts. Jesus. I'm like a rock for you. You hand me the bottle and I take a swig. You look me in the eye as you take your hand away from covering your pussy. Fuck me, it looks so sweet and juicy. Like an apricot bursting with joy. You eye me down while sliding a finger inside, then two. You start rubbing and pulling your nipples while I stroke for you. I want to taste and touch and fuck you so bad. Like my old cow Daisy when she was raring to eat some wet, thick, grass. You're breathing deeper as you finger your soaking pleasure pond and rub your clit. You pause and taste yourself off your fingers. Licking your lips. Closing your eyes and arching your back on the sink. "Taste my pussy," you tell me. I walk over and kiss your lips. Slowly down to your neck, licking your nipples, down your sexy stomach to your tanned thighs. Spreading your legs as my tongue lightly dances on your clit. Sliding up and down the side. It's throbbing and swollen. Flicking over and back on it. Lightly. Making it bigger. Making your apricot pleasure pond flow. I look up and see a bottle of rosé on the counter. I take some in my mouth and kiss your pussy. You grab my hair as you feel my tongue and the wine fill you up. Your wrap your legs around my head and shoulders as I eat you deeper and slower and wetter. Pushing your clit with my tongue. Fingering you and teasing your g-spot. Watching your ass grind on the sink as you moan and push my head and tongue deeper inside your pond of joy. You taste so fucking good. You start cumming as my tongue fucks you, moaning and grinding and gripping the sink. I look up and see you in heaven. You look at me and pull me up to kiss. We kiss fucking hard. You grab my cock and slide it inside. Sweet Jesus, my ponder pipe is in a dream. You feel like a warm wet cloud. You're grabbing my ass and pushing me deeper. I'm grabbing your neck and watching you close your eyes and moan for me. My rock hard cock filling you up. You climb off the sink and bend over facing the fridge. Fuck that. I open the fridge door and bend you half into it. You always wanted to be fucked in a fridge. I fuck you hard from behind. Cold air on our sweaty bodies. Slapping your ass hard as you moan louder and louder. It's so loud with the fridge echo. I grab a carrot from the door and put it in your mouth. Gagged by the carrot. I see both sides sticking out as I'm fucking you. You're a hot horse. You start to cum again and bite hard on the carrot. Fucking Christ, you neon delight. I cum with you, shooting hard inside. Fridge shaking as your scared cat runs to the bedroom. I stay hard and keep fucking you. Your sweet apricot pussy squeezing on my hard carrot cock. I cum again. You always want to taste it. You turn around with your tongue out. I cum on your wet lips as you swallow and suck me dry. Licking my balls. Kneeling on the kitchen floor and sucking every drop. You're a good girl. Malibu is burning. I hurt my hip. We broke the fridge. But fuck me, you're a hot neon fucker.

WET MONEY PUSSY

It's Wednesday night. Late. Dumb. It's windy. Irish has dumb politicians. So does America. Malibu is burning. It's sad. But I'm drunk. And so are you. I'm eating lettuce and you have pizza. Someone is spinning yarn. You're in your white body suit and red thong. You look so fucking hot. You've been talking to my friend all night. He's more famous than me. You love famous people. I thought you were going to fuck him. But then we started talking. And now we want to fuck. My friend doesn't know. But he would be pissed. This is naughty. You love it. Your body is too unreal. Your sexy brown eyes. Your big beautiful lips. Your hair. Fuck, I love your hair. You're too beautiful. It distracts from how smart. How talented. How much of a writer you are, you fucker. We meet late. No one is around. It's bad. We shouldn't. I walk inside your apartment and ask how long you've lived here. You jump up and wrap your legs around me. We haven't kissed in so long. I grab you against the wall and kiss you hard. You're amazing. I'm lost in your kiss as you grab my neck and stroke my cock, your legs wrapped around me. You have me in another world. I kiss you hard and choke your neck, kissing you against the wall. You lick my lips and ask what makes me cum nowadays. "Money," I tell you. Your eyes light up. You grab my cock and slide inside it your tight wet pussy. I slide you up and down my cock, your wet pussy dripping down onto my balls. You're rubbing your clit as I fuck you against the wall, your pussy soaking and your clit throbbing and swollen as it gets bigger and bigger. You slap my face and look at me as you're about to cum, then wrap your legs around me and fuck my hard wet cock up and down, deeper and deeper, harder and harder. "Have you seen my yarn?" you ask me. "What?" "My latex gloves?" "What the fuck-" "Where's my bicycle?!" I'm so confused as you start to cum on my cock. Jesus Christ. You're such a hot weird fuck. "Yo-yo me baby," you tell me, sliding up and down my cock. You slide deeper and slower on me, kissing my lips and pulling me close. I cum hard inside you, grabbing your hot red ass tight. I shoot deep as you bite your lip, telling me, "I have a fiancé." I cum again inside you as we kiss hard. It's windy. Malibu is burning. Politicians are dumb. It's sad. But you're the smartest hottest fucker I know. And I want you to write it all. You're a fucking vision. Let's booze. You eat a grape. And order more booze. Booze on.

RED BERRY PUSSY

We're in Paris. It's Monday and the weather is nippy. It's sad. Malibu is burning. Notre Dame is burning before our eyes. And I burnt my tongue on a cup of tea earlier in the day. So sad. My poor tongue. We just watched as the spire collapsed to the ground. You asked me to take some photos of you looking at it falling. You looked so beautiful in them. Wearing your French outfit. Black turtleneck, red miniskirt, black Air Force ones and raspberry beret. You wanted to wear heels but we were walking all day. I've been to Paris before so I didn't bother taking any photos of Notre Dame burning. I'll use old photos on Instagram, show people I've been here before, then they'll know why I'm so sad. I can't believe the damage. The poor Catholic Church. They're the good guys. The church was a symbol of hope. People say, back in the day, they burned every Jewish book in France in front of the church trying to get rid of Jews, but I don't believe them. It's hope. You even took a photo lifting up your mini skirt and showing your ass in the square. You said it'll make people feel less sad on Instagram. You're so hot and so right. The heat is making me sweat though. "Come with me," I tell you. You look up at me. Jesus. You're so pretty in front of the burning church. Your eyes are burning with delight. You're horny too. I kiss your lips on the banks of the Seine. You're so beautiful, your soft cheeks and wet lips, brushing your hair out of your eyes. Your eyes are prettier than all of Paris. You smile and feel my cock get hard against you. Rubbing your hand outside my jeans. Teasing your fingers up the shaft to the top. "Fuck me," you whisper in my ear. A fireman looks at us and smiles. He must know English. He runs towards the flames as I take you down the Seine. We kiss again on an old cobbled street. "I'm dripping," you tell me, smiling. I look around, it's just us. I pull you to a doorway and kiss you hard. You wrap a leg around me and I grab your hair. You bite your bottom lip as I kiss your neck. You smell so fucking good. I slide my fingers between your legs and feel your heat. Your pussy is wet and warm. Your clit is swollen and throbbing for me. Fuck. You have the sexiest red berry pussy. I want to taste. I start to finger you as we kiss. My hands getting wetter and wetter as you moan in my mouth. Your clit getting bigger and bigger as I rub it more and more. You grab my cock and take it out of my pants. Fuck, I'm rock hard for your French pussy. You tilt your head back and I put my hand on your neck. Your eyes close and lips smile. I hold your neck while fingering your soaked pleasure pond. It reminds me of the time Father O'Malley in Ireland would give us a bath after being altar boys. We were splashing and soaking. Now your pussy is soaking and splashing. A fire brigade drives me and I pull you close. You close your eyes as it drives by. You don't want to be caught. You're a good girl. "Come," I tell you, "I know where to go." I've been in Paris before. I'll never get over Notre Dame. But we're near my favourite café, Le Petit Mort. We enter, flush and horny. Hard and dripping. Heavy breathing. Hearts racing. Pussy tingling. I say hello to the owner, an old French man named Jean Pierre Papin. He smiles and says, "Two coffee, ice Americanos?" "Si," I tell him, "Gracias." He potters to the back of the kitchen to make coffee while I lead you by the hand to the bathroom. We have time. I take you inside the cramped bathroom and lock the door. You get on your knees and unzip my jeans. My rock hard ponder pipe flops out as you spit on it. You start to stroke and lick my cock, from my balls all the way to the tip. You have me soaked and rock hard. Fuck. You feel amazing as you start to suck and stroke, your raspberry beret bopping up and down. You're licking spit and precum off me as my cock gets harder and harder. I want to taste you. You stand up and face the sink, holding onto it. I lift up your skirt and taste your pussy from behind. You feel like a wet dream. You are the art in the gallery. You're the hottest woman in this city. And the wettest.

I'm licking your ass and pussy as you moan louder and louder. I need to gag you. I reach in your bag and take out the chocolate and baguette we bought earlier. You take off your beret and top as I'm feeding you chocolate. I love feeling your back, fucking you from behind. I put the baguette in your mouth as you chomp down. You're a good girl. It's the best ball gag we have. I slide my cock inside your tight, warm, pussy. Fuck. Feels amazing. Like a burning bog on a cold winter's day. Your pussy juice is dripping on me as I rub your clit and fuck you from behind. You're almost breaking the baguette in two. I feel your ass clench and squeeze, your pussy tightening on my cock. You moan loud as you cum hard with my cock deep inside you. Fuck. You're the hottest. I slap and grab your ass hard as I cum with you, shooting deep inside as you grind your ass on me, pushing me deeper, making me harder, making me cum again. Fuck. You're unreal. Malibu is burning. Notre Dame is burning. My tongue is on fire. It's sad. So sad. But that was so fucking hot. You red berry pussy. We must go buy you more chocolate. I hope the old man made the coffee iced. He better. Sweet Jean Pierre.

MILE NIGH CLUB

It's Monday. We're in San Fran. I'm tired. Shows all weekend. It's sad. Malibu is burning. Alabama is trying to take away women's right. Viagra is still allowed. Game of Thrones was weird. And we just saw a guy almost die at the airport. So sad. He was next to us eating a chicken sandwich. Not sure if he choked or had a heart attack. I did nothing. Just watched. Took a photo. I'm tired. At least the shows were good. We board the plane. I hope that guy is okay. Made me sweat watching him. Felt death in my body. Made me horny. You're looking too hot. Death is love. And love is deadly. You're wearing black leggings, black Nike AF 1s and a cream hoodie. You look casual and hot. As fuck. We're in the narrow hallway waiting to get on the plane. It's busy and cramped. You're standing in front of me. Too close. Rubbing your ass against my pants. I shouldn't have worn sweatpants flying. I'm going to be too hard. And can't hide it. I already got stopped at security because you had me hard walking in. They thought my ponder pipe was a weapon in my pants. You hot fucker. Your body is the weapon. You feel me get hard and start gently bouncing back harder against me. I put my hands under your hoodie on your lower back. Fuck. I shouldn't have touched you. Your skin drives me wild. So soft and sexy. I feel your body light up as you feel my hands wrap around your waist. You look over your shoulder at me and smile, biting your bottom lip. Your eyes are dancing. They want trouble. We are going to fuck. My ponder pipe is piping, like Pavarotti and the tenors in their prime. We shuffle our way onto the plane, smiling at the motherly stewardess. I have you close to me. You're now hiding how hard I am. You're my cock beard. I wonder if that guy died. Death by chicken. I almost choked on chicken before. That could've been me. Death. You. Chicken. I'm so fucking horny. We're on the emergency aisle. I'm the aisle seat and you're by the window. Balls. Forgot about middle seat. There's a Chinese girl in it. She's reading a big thick book, out loud, in Chinese. Splendid. I put our bags in the overhead and you discreetly grab my cock. You're a fucker. "I want it," you tell me. "What?" I ask dumbly, struggling with the bags. "Your hard cock inside my tight wet pussy." You said that too loud. But everyone is Chinese around us. "Let me taste it," you tell me, again too loud. I look around. Fuck it. I make my way to the bathroom, holding your hand. Everyone is preoccupied and doesn't seem to notice us making out like two horny teenagers waiting for the bathroom. I haven't made out like this since I snuck into the church cellar back in Ireland and kissed Mary O'Rourke in the dark. Two creepy cellar dwellers. Father O'Shea was just watching us from the stairs. So that was odd. She's a nun now too. Sister O'Rourke. The bathroom door swings open and a little Chinese man potters out. He has a name tag that says Tony. Okay. We both slide inside and lock the door. It's so fucking tight in here, like a fish's ass. You slide your hand inside my pants as I kiss your wet lips and sexy neck. I fucking love your neck. You're stroking my rock hard cock as

I feel how wet you are. Fuck. You're dripping. Death turns you on too. You somehow get to your knees and lick my cock, from the balls up along the shaft. I'm so turned on. I don't even know how you're managing to fit and do all that in this tight space, you're like a Brazilian soccer player with your ball work. You're sucking my balls and stroking my cock as you look me in the eye. Unreal. You rip off your hoodie and rub my cock between your tits. You're naked under the hoodie. I love you naked. Your body is the sexiest. You'd be a hot nun. You stand up and turn around, sliding your sweatpants down. Fuck me, your ass is insane. We're facing the mirror as I slide my cock inside your dripping wet pussy. You've the nicest pleasure pond. Like a nice cup of tea on a cold windy night. So warm and delightful. I put my hand on your neck and squeeze as my cock fills you up. Your eyes close as I squeeze harder. I kiss your shoulder and neck and ear. You're getting wetter and wetter. I bite and kiss your shoulder, squeezing your neck tighter as I rub your hard nipples. I feel how big and swollen your clit is for me. You moan and bite your lip hard as I tease and rub it more. I feel your pussy get wetter and tighter on my cock. You're going to cum. You're going to make me cum. Your ass and legs clench as your pussy tightens and you start cumming hard. Fuck. You're the most beautiful fucker alive. I cum with you, shooting hard and deep inside. We keep fucking as I feel your pussy drip down me. I cum again as you arch your back. Jesus. I grab your ass hard and squeeze your neck. I shoot again and you smile. You want to taste. You turn around and kiss me. I'm lost in you. You take my cock and rub your finger along the top. You smile and taste my cum. You hot fucker. You'd be a dancing cellar dweller. We leave the bathroom and I see the guy who I thought died. He's alive. Hallelujah. I catch Tony's eye. He smiles and says something in Chinese. Tony knows. "Oui oui," I tell him. That's my only Chinese. Pity we weren't in the air. No mile high. Mile nigh only. Ah well. Malibu is burning. Alabama is backwards. Game of Thrones was meh. And I'm even hornier than before. But at least that guy is alive. So that's nice. And now I'm dying for some chicken. Oui oui, Tony, oui oui.

RED VELVET THONG

It's Tuesday. I'm moving furniture into the spare room. It's sad. Malibu is burning. Tony Robbins has been cancelled. And I'm sweating. So sad. Two Mexican guys are helping me move the furniture, Sergio and Tom. We were getting in great until they broke a lamp. Then they stopped speaking English. Now we're working in silence and grunts. You arrive back as we're moving the bed frame. It's so heavy. It weighs the same as a dead cow. I remember lowering my old cow Connor into his grave back in Ireland when I was 7. This bed frame weighs the same. We need a break. Holy Jesus, you look unreal. You're in a white shirt and grey mini skirt. Fuck me pink. It's like school girl Britney Spears turned into a business woman. You look amazing. I'm in heat. Sweating. Hot. Horny. You smile at Sergio and Tom. They speak English again. "Hello, si, I am Mexican Tom." I hand Sergio a jug of freshly squeezed lemonade and tell him to take a break. Enjoy a jug on the roof. They both scuttle out the door as you look through your bag. "How was your day?" I ask. "I did jump rope and drew out some sketches and had a meeting..." I start kissing you as you speak. I can't help it. Your eyes are dancing and your big lips just drive me mental. I pick you up and place you on the kitchen counter. You're waist high to me. Just how I like you. I kiss your neck and unbutton your shirt as you tell me, "I went to the beach too." You moan and close your eyes as I open your shirt and kiss your neck. My lips on your collar bone. My hands on your lower back. Sliding your shirt off. Running my hand through your hair. Grabbing the back of your head. You biting your lip as I grab your hair harder. I kiss your lips again, hand on your neck. You wrap your legs around me and press your body against mine. Fuck. I love your hard nipples on me. I take off my t-shirt and pull your body close to mine. I love kissing your big lips. They're so lovely and soft, like a bucket of butter that's been left in the sun for too long. You're my hot bucket of butter. I want to taste how wet you are for me. See if you're melting. "What underwear are you wearing?" I ask, squeezing your neck. You love it. You're a good girl. The best butter. "Red velvet," you say. My favourite. "Kneel on the counter," I tell you. You look at me then do as you're told. You get on your hands and knees, and face away from me on the counter. You know what do you. You look over your shoulder at me as I lift up your skirt. Massaging your sexy legs. Rubbing your beautiful ass. I love your legs and ass. They're like Laurel and Hardy. My favourite. I kiss the back of your legs, moving my lips up to your ass cheeks. Sliding your skirt all the way up until I see your red velvet thong. Better than any cake. I spread your legs and kiss your thighs, opening them wider. You arch your back and moan as my lips kiss your thong. You're soaking wet for me. You're a good girl. I tease your pussy and kiss your thighs. You feeling my breath on your hot pussy. Sliding your soaked thong down your sexy legs. I start kissing your ass cheeks and hear your moan, my tongue getting closer to your dripping pleasure pond. You want me to taste. I slide my tongue inside your pussy and feel your bucket of butter overflow. You soak my mouth with how wet you are. My tongue slides deep inside and I feel you get wetter and wetter. I grab and slap your ass, then slide my tongue inside your tight wet pussy again. In and out. Slow and deep. Wetter and wetter. Clit getting bigger and bigger. Teasing you that I'm going to touch it. Your legs quivering. Arms shaking. Tongue fucking you from behind. Your ass grinding in my face. My tongue sliding inside and hearing you moan louder. Your arms shaking harder to keep balance. My tongue teasing your tight ass. Fucking your wet pussy. The hottest fucking bucket of butter there is. I run my tongue along your pussy finally up to your clit. I lightly lick it and you moan deep and loud. It's so swollen for me. My tongue riverdances on your clit, driving you insane. Right then there's a knock at the door, "Si senór, it's Mexican Tom. Can we have more lemonade?" I turn you around and pick you up. Carry you to the laundry room. "Yes, Mexican Tom, help yourself." I hear him enter as I lock the laundry door. You're sitting on the washing machine. Rubbing your clit. Legs spread. Pussy dripping. "Who said you could touch yourself?" I ask. You put your hands on the washer and bite your lip. You're so close to cumming, I can tell. I take my rock hard cock out of my pants. You start stroking it as I kiss your butter lips again. I squeeze your neck as you close your eyes. I reach behind you and turn on the washing machine. It starts to whirl and vibrate. You start to breathe deeper and deeper. Louder and louder. You're going to cum from the machine. You grab my cock and slide it inside your soaking pussy. Fuck. You feel like heaven. I can't believe it's not butter. My cock fills you up and you gasp and moan. You wrap your legs around me as I choke you harder. Your head leaning back. Eyes closed. Smiling and moaning. Machine vibrating. Clit throbbing. Mexican Tom drinking lemonade. Your pussy tightens on me as you start to cum hard. I choke tighter and you almost pass out. You gasp for air and cum again, even harder. I grab your ass tighter to me and fuck you deeper. Washing machine vibrating on my cock and balls. Feels like I'm being licked by a cow. I think of cows and cum hard inside you. Fucking Christ. Your legs and arms wrapped around me as I shoot again. I stay hard and fuck you, like two wild beasts. Kissing and cumming and fucking. You take my cum in your mouth as you drop to your knees. Your butter lips on my butter balls. It's sad. Malibu is burning. Tony is over. Now I'm sweating way more. But at least we have lemonade. And you're my bucket of butter. Mexican Tom knocks on the door, "Senõr, we must go, back tomorrow." Ciao ciao, I tell him, ciao ciao, the only Spanish I know.

NUDE PUMP ON

It's Wednesday. We're in New York. I forgot my jacket. It's raining. So sad. Malibu is burning. My hair is wet. It was sunny in L.A. I forgot it's a big country. So sad. And we're late. Meeting your friends at a restaurant somewhere in East Village. I never know where anywhere is. But you're looking radiant. Glowing. You are a supermodel amongst supermodels in New York. You beautiful fucker. Your white linen shirt, skinny black jeans and black boots. And your cool leather jacket. I'm considering asking you if I can borrow it. Everywhere was shut. Couldn't buy one.

I'll just drink whiskey. It'll warm me up. You have a bottle of wine for your friend's birthday. You used to be a sommelier at the restaurant we're going to, back when you lived here. "How do you spell sommelier again?" I ask you. "I always forget," you say. "Me too," I say, "Som-mel-ier. Like summer liar?" Living in L.A. has made me dumb. We get to the spot, Freddie's Finest, an upmarket Italian-Indian cuisine place. Michelin star rated. I hope they have porridge. You look so fucking hot as the host greets us. I want to kiss your big beautiful lips. "Come here," I tell you. You smile and pucker. I kiss you, too deep. See those stars from a good kiss. Ah fuck. We're both horny. I can tell. You grab me and kiss me again. Feels like a good minute kiss. The hostess, Debra, is just looking at us. I like that name, good Italian name. We are just standing in the entrance kissing. Your nipples are hard through your white linen shirt. Fuck. My cock is hard through my black jeans. I grab the back of your neck as I kiss you. You breathe deep and moan. You're lost now too. "Is the cloak room still downstairs?" you ask Debra. "Oh to be sure," she replies. "We'll be right back," you say with a smile. You grab my hand and lead me down the narrow stairs, rubbing my cock as we go. You're a hot fucking deviant. I like it. We walk past a room with a sign saying PUMP ROOM. "Oh we have to fuck in there," I tell you. "No. That's where they pump the bathroom pipes out to the sewer," you reply. "Cloak room." "Okay," I nod, "Wise woman. Pump on." You lead me inside the narrow room. Like a walk-in closet. Surrounded by jackets. I spot a couple I might take by mistake. You lock the door and stand against it. Fuck. You look so fucking sexy. I want to eat and ravage and dominate you, like a warm shepherd's pie on a crisp winter's day. You are mince and gravy. You're the hottest mashed potatoes. Fuck. I'm so horny. You politely take off your jacket and hang it up. You're a good girl. You stand at the door. Waiting. I walk up to you and pause. Look at you in the eyes. You're fucking amazing. I love your mighty brain. I can feel it staring at me. I kiss your soft lips hard. Your head hits the door and you wrap your arms around me. Fuck. You feel so good. I undo your shirt and then mine. Your boobs are tear drops of joy. The hottest drops of rain. I love them. I undo your bra and kiss you again, feeling your hard nipples. You breathing deeper as I softly tease them. Kissing your neck and ear. You undoing my pants. Me unzipping your jeans. Kissing your shoulder as you pull my hard cock out of my pants. It's rock hard for you. It always is. You bend down and start sucking me slowly. Kissing my cock and playing with my balls. I'm in a sea of coats and a heaven of delight. Your mouth is like a warm potato pie. You spit on my cock and suck faster and deeper. I'm so wet and hard, like a wall on a rainy day. I pull your hair back as you suck. You look at me and ask, "Am I a good girl?" You are a good fucking girl. Jesus, you're hot. I pull you up and kiss your lips. Push you against the door and squeeze your neck. You're a good fucking girl. Your wet lips are driving me insane. I want you wetter. I pull your jeans down as far as your boots. Your sexy nude thong is soaked. You think nude is boring. It's not. You look hot in everything. It's you, you hot fucker. You'd look hot in a diaper. I pull your thong down past your knees and taste your wet pussy. It's so fucking nice, like a wet plum on rainy Friday. You're overflowing for me. Your clit is swollen and throbbing in my mouth. Your pussy is dripping down my chin. Jesus. You're soaked. I want to fuck you. I lick your clit and grab your ass cheeks. Playing with your ass with my wet finger. "Open the wine bottle," I tell you. You always have a wine opener. You open it and hand it to me. I stand up and take a mouthful. You drink some too. We kiss and drink another. You hand me the cork and smile. I rub it along your soaked pussy. It's soaked now too. I hand it back and smile. You know what to do. I take another mouthful and kiss your pussy again. You are the sweetest wine. Good for my heart. Two buck chuck, that's Trader Joe's wine. You take the cork and push it into your tight ass. You clench and push your pussy into my face. My tongue goes deeper inside as I push the cork inside your ass. A little cork plug. That's staying in there for the night. You moan as I run my tongue over your swollen clit. You want me inside of you. I stand up and kiss your lips again. Bite your shoulders. Squeeze your neck. "You're a good girl," I tell you, then take a hand and tie it with a jacket to the top coat rail. You place your left hand on the other rail and

I do the same. Now you're all mine. Corked and tied up. I slide my hard cock inside you as your eyes light up and then close. You smile and breathe deep as my cock goes deeper inside your soaking pleasure pond. My ponder pipe is in full flow. Fucking you deep while I squeeze your neck. "Harder," you whisper. I choke you harder and fuck you deeper. Your stomach and legs are quivering, like a fiddle that's just been played. Your arms are pulling at the rails as you get closer to cumming. I choke you harder and rub your clit as your breathe deeper and slower. "You're a bad girl," I say in your ear, choking you as you start to cum for me. You almost pass out as you cum hard. Your legs and arms tied. Your body mine. Your lips kissing me. "I'm a bad girl," you whisper back, making me harder and fuller. I start to cum inside you as I lift you up. I shoot deep inside and kiss your lips. "Come for me" you say in my ear. I shoot hard again. Fuck me you're amazing. You clench your ass to keep the cork in. I cum again and kiss you hard. There's a knock at the door. Debra? "How do you like the closet?" "Lovely," I tell her, "Coming." We kiss again and I untie you. We dress and go upstairs to meet your friends. Malibu is burning. It's sad. I've no jacket. But that was a great pump room. And you've a cork in your ass. "I'm from Cork," I tell Debra. She smiles and starts speaking Indian and Italian telling us the main dishes. "Porridge, bitte, danke," I tell her. It's the only Indian I know.

WET WHISKEY PUSSY

It's Sunday. The day of our Lord. The Sabbath. The holiest day. I'm drunk. We both are. It's sad. Malibu is burning. The weather is weird. And I'm horny and drunk during the day. So sad. Sorry, God. I blame you. You've looked beautiful and sexy all day long. We were at brunch. You were in your striped blue and white dress. I ordered too many eggs. Your friend doesn't like me. Allister. He thinks I slept with his girlfriend before. I didn't, but she tried. He tried to mock my t-shirt saying it looked old and cheap. I had to tell him it was new and expensive. We sat in silence like two losers. You laughed at me and drank more champagne. The way you drink from a glass always turns me on. I don't know why. You're just the hottest fucker. With the most beautiful lips. I want to kiss them all the time. We went to a rooftop pool and drank some more. Your buddy told me he was staunch pro life. I knew he was an asshole. Allister the Asshole I called him. You were dazzling in the water. Your black bikini and slicked back hair. I was hard just looking at you. You kept telling me to come into the water but I couldn't stand up. Too many people. Me just waltzing around with a hard cock. You knew it and kept telling everyone to get me to come in. You're a true prick. I like it. And now we are at a dive bar. Ditched your buddies and the fancy life. Sitting in a booth. Drinking pickle backs. Whiskey. Pickle juice. And you have wine. Just two classy clowns. Your lips are wet from the whiskey. I fucking love them. Your neck looks so good. I want to squeeze. You seem to know. Keep teasing me with it. Your collar bone too. I want my hand pressing on it as I fuck you. "I like your collar bone," I tell you. "It's called a clavicle," you tell me. You're a real fucker. I'm a fan. "Sorry, clavicle. I like your clavicle, you fucker." I cheers your whiskey and we do a shot. You lean over and kiss me with your wet whiskey lips. Fuck. It's heaven. Your hand on my crotch. Feeling my hard cock. Squeezing through my pants. I kiss you harder. "What do you want to do to me?" you ask. "I want my hand pressing on your clavicle and neck while I'm fucking you hard," I reply with a smile. "Well then do it." You take my hand and guide it between your legs, sliding up your dress. You're not wearing underwear. You're so fucking wet. I rub your clit and watch you bite your bottom lip, then slide a finger inside. You close your eyes and moan as I slide two inside your wet whiskey pussy. You're like a bucket of lard on a hot summer's day, dripping and drenched and ready to be fucked. "Bathroom," I tell you. You smile and taste my fingers. You're a good girl. You go to the back of the dive bar. I follow you a minute later. Had to tuck my boner up. Thanks, belt. Everyone at the bar is sad and depressed. Like a long line of Bukowskis. Waiting for the day to die. Sundays are fun. I knock on the door and slip inside. You pounce on me, kissing me hard. I lock the door and pick you up, pushing you against the sink. Kissing your lips and neck and collar bone. Slipping your dress off at the shoulders. Sliding it down your body to your waist. Running my lips down your body. Kissing your perfect boobs. Your hard nipples. Teasing. Biting. Harder. Kissing your sexy stomach. Down to your legs. Pulling your dress up. Licking around your wet whiskey pussy. Slowly kissing your thighs. Closer and closer to your soaking pleasure pond. Feeling the heat from the bucket of lard. Running my tongue over your swollen clit. Throbbing on my lips as I kiss and flick and lick. Teasing your pussy lips, like a sexual bully. Tormenting your clit and driving you insane. Grabbing my hair as my tongue slides inside and tastes how sweet you are. You're a real true feck, but you've the nicest pussy. Gushing like a geyser in my mouth. You're a fucking geezer. Moaning and breathing hard. Ass clenching and legs trembling. My fingers inside and tongue on your clit. Getting wetter and wetter for me. Dripping down your sexy legs. All over me. Grabbing my head as you start to cum in my mouth. Your clit so swollen as you cum hard. You're so fucking wet. I'm so fucking hard. I stand up and kiss your lips. You're gasping and want more. I undo my pants as you stroke my cock. You take it and slide it inside. I squeeze your neck as I fill you up. Your eyes roll and lips smile. I kiss your lips and shoulder as I fuck you against the sink. Hand pressing on your fucking clavicle. Choking you harder. You love it. You're a good girl. Pussy flooding on my rock hard cock. Deeper inside. You're lost in it. Warm wet whiskey. Pouring on me. I choke you harder and feel your pussy tighten on my cock. I rub your clit with my other hand and you start to cum again for me. You're a hot fucker. I bite your shoulder as I cum with you. Shooting deep inside your pond. My ponder pipe singing like a flute. Fucking as we kiss. Two drunk lovers. Loving it. You pull my cock out and start sucking. I cum hard again as you swallow it all. You're a good fucking girl. Malibu is burning. Your friend's a prick. I think I got sunburnt. But that was hot. Although we forgot to go to Mass. Sorry, God. Forgive me Jesus. Fuck me pink. Let's have some whiskey.

STRAWBERRY FIELDS

It's Wednesday. And hot. And I'm horny. The sink is blocked. The pipes are burst. Malibu is burning. It's sad. So sad. You're trying on dresses. The plumber is in the kitchen. I'm waiting for him to leave so I can go to the gym. A lot's going on. And you keep stripping naked in front of me asking which dress I prefer for your fancy dinner. "The blue one," I tell you. They all seem blue. Or black. With thigh high slits. And your hot legs. Is the AC not on? Why am I so hot? And horny? You want to know what underwear looks better under the blue dress. "Black?" You walk out of the bedroom in your black thong and bra. Fuck. You're so sexy. I think I've been so turned on because you were reading with me while waiting for the plumber. A physics book. Your brain drives me mental. It's so mighty. And such a feck. And with your body. It's too much. I want to fuck you. I want to fuck you stupid. Make you see how dumb I feel around you. It's the best. "Or the red?" you ask. Oh the red is fucking hot too. You turn around. Jesus your ass is like a red baby potato in that thong. I love baby potatoes. Now I want to eat your ass. You turn back around. I can't stop staring at your crotch. Looks like a red strawberry. I want to taste how sweet. You look amazing. "Senór? You pour coffee into garbage disposal?" Pedro asks. Pedro the Plumber. I had to hire him. "No," I say, lying. "Looks like coffee," he says. "Maybe she did?" I say, blaming you. You fake shock and swivel away. I'm trying to look at you in the bedroom and Pedro in the kitchen at the same time. Just in case either of you needs a hand. Pedro seems fine. I turn to check on you. You're just sitting on the bed, naked, wearing your new tanned Nike. I picked them out. They're savage. You're savage. "Jesus Christ," I said too loud. "I know senór, so much coffee." I try to say something to Pedro but you beckon me over to you. I come and kiss you while you sit on the bed. You moan

98

as I grab your neck and kiss your soft lips. "This is my favourite outfit," I say. You smile as I squeeze your neck tighter. You love my hand on your throat. In control. You smile and close your eyes as I squeeze tighter. I lick your lips and you open your eyes and mouth. Sticking your tongue out. You're a bad girl. I spit in your mouth and you swallow and smile. Door wide open. The clank of Pedro's tools on the pipes. My hard ponder pipe popping out of my gym shorts. You reach and start to stroke it through the shorts, then pull and flop it out. It's so fucking hard for you. Like a difficult sum on a maths exam. I love sums. You love my cock. You spit on it and stroke it slowly. You look at me and I take my hand off your neck. You lick the top of my cock, like an ice cream cone down at the beach. Licking it up and down as it drips in your mouth. Taking it inside as you suck it deep and wet. Taking it out hard and dripping for you. Sucking my balls as you slowly stroke it, getting faster and faster. The wet squelch in time with the clanking pipes. Fuck. My precum on your lips. You pulling back. Your spit sticking to my cock then flopping onto your chin. Down onto your beautiful boobs. I want to taste you. I spit in your mouth again and kiss your lips. You smile and close your eyes as I push you to lay on the bed. My tongue running down your neck and wet boobs. Your hard nipples with some of your spit of them. Me kissing it off. Flicking your nipples. Biting softly on them. Licking and kissing down your sexy stomach. Grabbing your ass as I kiss your thighs. Your soft peach thighs. I love them. Closer and closer. To your cabbage patch. The field or gold. Strawberry lane. Like a ripe berry waiting for a firm touch. Waiting to burst. My lips on your pussy lips. Like pillows of pussy. So soft and juicy. My tongue on your clit. Softly. Teasing. Pressing. Touching. Firmer. Pushing. Harder. You moaning. Louder. Grabbing a pillow. Biting it. Door open. Pedro. Might hear. Your strawberry pussy bursting in my mouth. Flooding down your legs. Like a river's banks bursting open. Your ass getting wet. My finger sliding inside. Fingering your tight asshole as my tongue drives your clit wild. Swollen. Throbbing. Begging. Wanting to cum. Kissing your clit while I finger your pussy. Beckoning. Two fingers. Cum for me. Your clit in my mouth. Your ass clenching. Tightening. Soaked. Flooding. Starting so squirt in my mouth. You're so fucking hot. Shouting into the pillow as you squirt for me. Your pussy lost in ecstasy. Your whole body shaking as you cum again hard for me. Back arching. Ass gripping. Pulling at the sheets. Your soaked pussy begging for my cock. Sliding inside you. Fingering your wet ass as I fuck you deep. You sucking my finger as your pussy takes my cock deeper. Choking your sexy neck. I love your neck. Open your mouth. You take my spit again. You love it. Being dominated. Taken. Fucked. I spank your ass. Your legs shake again as you cum again for me. I press the pillow in your face as I cum with you. Shooting hard and deep inside you. You feeling and loving it. Ass lifting off the bed. Me shooting again. Your thighs trembling. Me pulling my cock out and shooting again on your body. Your perfect tits. Fucking Jesus. You're unreal. The hottest fucker alive. Malibu is burning. The pipes are gone. It's sad. But you. And Pedro. He's calling me. You tanned delight

GREY CALVINS

It's Friday. You're angry. It's hot. Malibu is burning. The bees are dying. The ice is melting. And I have the worst hangover. It's sad. So sad. But you look so fucking hot. Your black crop top and black yoga pants. Your new white Nike. Jesus. You're a weapon. "Are you still angry?" I ask. "Yes. Fuck you." Nice. I was meant to meet you at a karaoke bar to meet your friends who are in town. But I got drunk after a show. And forgot to come. "You're an asshole." "Thank you" I reply with a smile. "No fuck you, I mean it," you tell me. "I want to fuck you." "You're not fucking me. Fuck off." "Oh I am. Then you won't be angry." You walk past me out of the bedroom. I grab you and pull you to me. "Get off me," you say, heated up. I push you against the wall and look in your eyes. "No," I tell you. You're so fucking angry. And heated. And turned on. It's hot. You want to fight me. You try to hit out but I grab your hand and pin it behind your back, hard. I have you pinned against the wall. Hand on your neck. Squeezing. Harder. Your anger mixing with wanting to be fucked. Trying to break free. I kiss your lips and you try to bite my bottom one. You fucker. I grab your hair and yank your head back. "Don't do that again," I tell you. "I'm a bad girl," you reply. You fucking are. I slap your face and you smile. You like it. Good girl. I start to squeeze your neck as your hand reaches for my cock. I rip down your yoga pants and push you harder against the wall. You're so fucking wet. You need to be fucked. Your grey Calvin Klein are soaked through. They're my favourite underwear of yours. You sexy fucker. Stroking my cock as I pin you hard. Pulling down your thong. Feeling your swollen clit. Moaning as I rub it. "You like that?" I ask you. "Yes Daddy," you reply. Good girl. I squeeze your neck and rub your clit. It's like a mango ready to fly. You want my cock inside you. I kiss your lips again. You bite me again, you fuck. I slap you. Harder. You moan and breathe deeper. Fuck you. I slide my hard cock inside your tight drenched pussy. Fuck. I love your angry pussy. My cock filling you up. Fucking you deep. Pinned against the wall. Like a hot bad girl. I slap your face again. Just because. You like it. I fuck you harder. I want you. You can barely breathe. Choking your neck. Squeezing the sides. You getting light headed. I grab your face and tell you, "Open your mouth." You do as you're told. I spit in your mouth and fuck you harder. "Again." You open and I spit again. You close and swallow. "You like that?" You smile and nod your head. "Are you going to be a good girl?" You nod again. I spin you around and pin you face first against the wall. My body weight pressing against you as I fuck you from behind. My hard cock sliding up and down. Deeper inside your soaked pussy. Rubbing your clit with one hand. My right hand on your throat. Choking. Fucking. Soaking. "I'll be a good girl Daddy," you say into the wall. "Good girl," I tell you, then spank your ass hard. You moan and legs start to shake. I rub your clit and fuck you deeper. Feeling you cum on my cock. Pinned against the wall. Cumming for me like a good girl. You turn your face to the side and open your mouth. I spit again and you lick it off your lips then swallow. Your ass slapping off my thighs. Cock so fucking hard for you. You push back harder on my cock. I squeeze your neck tighter and spank your ass cheek hard. I start to cum inside you. Shooting deep as you grind on my cock. I spin you around and keep fucking. Your legs wrapped around me now. Against the wall. Hard and cumming inside. I take my cock out and you drop to your knees. Sucking our cum off my cock. I shoot again and you take it on your tongue and lips. You're a good girl. Malibu is burning. The bees. The ice. The honey. You were angry. Not any more. "I'm going to yoga," you tell me, pulling up your soaked thong. You're a bad fucking girl.

PURPLE THONG

It's Monday. My brain is dead. I'm goosed from the night before. Malibu is burning. It's sad. So sad. You had an audition this morning. Didn't have time to masturbate. You have the brain fog too. I come over and you're already in bed. Walk in your apartment door straight to your room. You're trying to nap. Naked body. Just wearing your purple thong. I strip down to my boxers and climb on the bed. You roll over and I climb on top of you. Kissing your sexy lips. Feeling your hot sex hair. Grabbing it. Kissing your neck. Your hands on my back. Nails digging in. My hand starting to squeeze your neck as I kiss and bite your shoulder. My hard cock rubbing against your thong. Your pussy getting wetter and wetter. I bite your shoulder hard and your nails dig into me. Too hard. I slap your face and you smile. "Open your mouth." You do as you're told and I spit inside. I kiss your lips and down your neck. Your hard nipples on my tongue. Your back arching. My lips going down your stomach. Inside your thighs. Feeling your warm pussy. Pulling off your thong. Down your sexy legs. Sliding off my boxers. Your legs spread open for me. Moaning and back arching. Wanting my tongue on your clit. Your pussy dripping. My lips kissing your lips as you moan and pussy bursts, like an over ripe flowery potato. My tongue slides deep inside and moves up to your swollen clit. Feeling it throb on my tongue. Your pussy getting wetter than a rainy day in June. So tight and warm and soaked. Like Niagara Falls in my mouth. You taste so fucking good. You start to cum in my mouth as I finger your tight ass and lick your swollen clit. I'm so fucking hard for you. I'm going to fuck you dumb. You grab my head and I come to kiss you. My mouth dripping with your pussy juice. You lick it up as I spit in your mouth again. I slap your face and slide my cock inside your tight pussy. You moan and wrap your legs around me. I go deeper and lift your back up off the bed. I fuck you hard while choking your sexy neck. Your eyes closed and moaning for me. "You fucking like that you hot fucker," I say in your ear. "Yes Daddy," you tell me. You're a good girl. I slap your face and fuck you harder. Your wet pussy drenched on my hard cock. Pulling on your hard nipples. Dominating your sexy body. Your brain fog gone. My hard cock ready to burst. You start to cum again for me and my cock feels your pussy tighten. I slap your ass hard and grab your tiny waist. I cum hard and deep inside you. Fucking Jesus. I'm lost in you. I shoot again and kiss your wet lips. You open your mouth and I spit inside. I take out my cock and you suck the rest of the cum out of me. You're a hot fucker. You swallow it and smile. "Thanks Daddy." Malibu is burning. But you're a good girl.

YOGA PANTS

It's Wednesday. I've been stuck on the phone for an hour with my visa lawyer. It's brutal. Malibu is burning. I'm starving. Phone calls are the worst. So sad. I can't even remember what we're talking about. But I'm frustrated. And have to go. You walk in the door after going for a run. Up Runyon. It's so hot out. I should have went. But I had this call. I needed a sweat. I fucked up. You're glowing and looking so hot. Drinking water in the kitchen. Your black sports bra and black Alo yoga pants and new Nike Flyknit shoes. You hot fucker. My lawyer Bob is asking me some inane question as you come over and kiss me. You know I'm annoyed. I pull you closer and feel the sweat on your back. You rub my cock and I'm immediately hard. I want to fuck you dumb. You keep kissing me, harder and like a true sexy fucker. You love doing it when I'm on the phone. I grab your neck and look at you in the eyes. You're so fucking beautiful. I squeeze and your eyes close. Look at those lips. I want them on my hard cock, like an avocado on toast, or a potato on porridge. Bob asks again, "Can I confirm that?" "Yes," I say into the phone as I watch you undress for me. Slipping out of the Nike. Peeling down your tight pants. Taking off your bra. Turning around and sliding off your black thong for me. I spank your ass hard. You turn around and smile. Tanned and sexy and sweaty. You're a fucking weapon. I lean against the dining room table as you take my top off. Kissing down my body as you pull down my pants. My hard cock flopping out as you kiss my stomach and undress me too. I'm naked on the phone to my lawyer. He won best lawyer of the year the last three years in a row. This is an expensive call. Your lips and tongue on my balls. Spitting on my cock. Stroking it while you're on your hands and knees. Taking my cock deep in your mouth, like an oven opening up to take a chicken. I love roast chicken. Reminds me of my hen when I was growing up, Henry. She ran away with a sheep. Wild times. I love you sucking my cock though. You're the blowjob Queen. Getting my ponder pipe drenched in spit and precum. Down to my balls. Stroking and sucking. Me grabbing the back of your head and fucking you like a dirty little whure. You like that. Gagging on it until you can barely breathe. Taking it out so I can slap it off your cheeks and lips. Bob asking me questions. You saying "Sorry, Daddy," then taking it in your mouth again. Calling you a good girl. I like how wet you get giving me a blowjob. You're kneeling over my foot and I can feel your pussy dripping. So fucking hot. Rubbing your clit with my foot as you suck and feel your nipples. You rub your pussy and show me how wet your fingers are. "Suck it," I tell you. "Pardon?" Bob asks. "Nothing," I say, watching you suck your fingers and touch yourself. I want to fuck you. You have my cock ready to burst, like a sausage left on the frying pan. I take you by the neck and stand you up. Kiss your wet pussy lips. You're a fucking fruit. I turn you around and bend you over the table. Rubbing your ass and back softly, then slapping your ass cheek hard and firm. You grip the table bent over and moan. I rub softly then spank again. I tease my finger over your asshole and along your pussy. You're fucking drenched, like you were caught in the November rain. You'll catch a cold. I mute Bob and spank you harder. "I want your cock, Daddy," you say. I spank harder and push your lower back, arching your ass up. "Please," you say again. I spank harder, your perfect ass red. You have the nicest ass I've ever felt or seen. Should be in a museum. I slide my cock inside your slippery wet pussy. Fuck. The tightest wettest warmest. I pin you to the table and fuck you hard. Deeper and deeper. Grinding against the wooden table. Your face pushed into it. Bob listing out legal issues. Me fucking so hard inside you. I rub your swollen clit and feel your pussy tighten. "Come for me," I tell you. Your body shakes as you cum like a good girl. I grab your hair and you turn your head. I spit in your mouth and squeeze your neck. You're trying to grip the table as I fuck you deeper and deeper. I flip you around, legs on my shoulders, hand on your neck, squeezing hard, your mouth open. I slap your face and spit in your mouth. "More." You're a good girl. I slap harder and spit again. You start to cum again and I slap harder. I choke your neck as I cum deep inside, shooting hard. We keep fucking and kissing. You open your mouth. I spit again. You're a good girl. I pull out and cum on your stomach. You open your mouth and I cum again, shooting on your nipples and face. You smile and feel it with your fingers. Malibu is burning. Bob is talking. I forgot to put it on mute. It's sad. But you're a sexy girl. You hot fucker.

WHITE CAPRIS

It's Monday. It's so fucking hot. Like so hot. I can't hack this heat. Especially hungover. Malibu is burning. The sea is full of plastic. I spent $25 on hotdogs last night drunk. It's sad. So sad. I just picked you up. You had a fitting and a class. I like your outfit. How aren't you sweating and I am? We're sitting in the car in a Coffee Bean car park. In the corner. Kind of hidden away. It's usually busier but today seems quiet. The parking guy, Freddie Franco, asked if we needed a ticket. "I'll come get it," I tell him. You pump the AC for me while you do your lipstick in the mirror. I like watching you. Your mouth half open. I'm so dumb. Whenever I see that I want to kiss you and have you suck my cock. I'm a real creep. You are too. "Give me a kiss," I tell you. You roll your eyes and kiss me. You know I'm ruining your lipstick. But we kiss hard. The heat. Has us horny. You. Always have me horny. You climb on top of me as we kiss. I push the seat back as you undo your bra. Kissing your neck and taking off your black and white top. I love you topless. You're fucking beautiful. Like a plate of potatoes on a sad rainy day. Or like a pub in the middle of nowhere. Your perfect hard nipples. Your teardrop boobs. And your stomach. Jesus. Unreal. Thanks, Pilates. I grab your hair and look at you. Your piercing eyes. Like a pierced ear piercing. Pierce me. "Pierce me," I tell you. "What?" "I don't know, the heat, I can't think." You slide down me onto the floor on your knees. Take my rock hard cock out of my jeans and spit on it. You lick it up and down the shaft, getting it wetter and wetter. "Slide your pants down," I tell you. You do as you're told, unzipping your white capris and sliding them down. You look so fucking sexy on your knees, in your white lace thong, like the hottest nun I've ever seen. Reminds me of Sister Betty back in Ireland. She was a stunning nun. You start to rub your clit as you suck my cock. Taking it all in your mouth and throat. Choking and gagging on it. Spit dripping off it. Stuck to your lipstick lips. Sucking my balls and stroking my cock. Rubbing your clit for me like a good girl. I take my cock out and slap it off your face. "You're a good girl," I tell you when you open your mouth for me. I spit and you start sucking my cock again. Licking off the precum. I look in the rear view mirror. A couple are walking to their car. I don't care. You're sucking me too good. "Keep going," I tell you. I see Freddie Franco looking

over at the car but he's old, he can't see. "Come here," I tell
you. You climb up, rubbing your soaked white lace thong on my
hard cock as you kiss me. I squeeze your neck and slap you.
You smile, like a true creep. I want to taste you. I recline the
chair fully and you keep climbing. Almost sitting on my face as
I kiss your stomach and slide your thong down your legs. I kiss
your thighs and slide my tongue over your swollen clit. Firmly
running it up and down. Getting it bigger and bigger. You're
fucking beautiful. I taste your wet pussy as my tongue slides in
and your juice bursts out. You moan and grab the roof. You're
too loud. I keep eating your pussy as you get louder and louder.
Fuck. I want to feel your wet pleasure pond on my rock hard
dancing ponder pipe. You slide down me and my cock slides
straight inside your tight pussy. You're so wet and warm, like a
bed that I mistakenly pissed in. I choke your neck and slap your
firm peach ass as you ride on my cock. You're a good girl, I tell
you, fucking you hard and choking your pretty neck. Grinding
on me. Riding me. Ass slapping off my thighs. "Turn around," I
tell you. You swivel around and start fucking me reverse car girl
style. Looking over your shoulder at me. Sexy fucker. I love your
hot back. Toned and tight and beautiful. I spit on your back and
you fuck harder. I take a seatbelt and use it to restrain your arms
behind your back. You like it and start moaning louder. I take
the other seatbelt and gag your mouth with it. Now you're silent
and dripping and fucking me like you're about to cum hard. I
rub your clit and play with your nipples. Fucking you reverse
car girl. Your muffled moans in the seatbelt. Body shaking.
Slapping your ass. Pulling your hair. Hard afternoon car fucking
as your ass clenches and releases as you cum hard for me. I can
feel it dripping on me. So fucking hot. You keep grinding and
squeezing on my cock. Tight pussy so fucking wet. I start to
cum hard with you. Shooting deep inside. Kissing your back as I
cum. Pulling on the seatbelts. Shooting hard again. Fuck. You're
unreal. I untie you and you turn around and start kissing me,
then slide down and lick my cock clean. You're a good girl. I see
Freddie Franco walking over to the car again. I slip the car into
reverse and he stops walking. You climb into the passenger seat

and I start to drive away. Malibu is burning. Forgot to get coffee. It's sad. Although now we're driving home naked. And you're sucking my cock again. You're a good fucking nun.

METALLICA JESUS

It's Sunday. The day of our Lord. Hi, Jesus. I'm hungover. Thanks, Jesus. Malibu is burning. Sweet, Jesus. Kids are in concentration camps. We're at Mass. It's sad. So sad. That's how bad my hangover is. I forced us back to religion. You laughed and said you would come to watch me sweat in church. I've been horny the entire time. You dressed too hot. Tight blue jeans with black boots and your black Metallica shirt, all tied up. Showing off your hot stomach. You're a fucking weapon. I'm trying to focus on Father O'Toole's lovely sermon. He's waffling on about Nazareth while I'm trying to not think about bending you over the pew and fucking you in front of God. Slapping a Bible off your sexy ass. Father O'Toole starts singing Our Father and I join in. I'm trying to not think about how hard I am for you. While I'm warbling, I feel your hand on my crotch. "You're a bad man," you whisper in my ear. Sends a shiver down my spine and makes me harder. "I know," I whisper back, putting my hand on your lower back. You moan and breathe in. You know we're going to fuck. I sing louder and try to not think about how hard my cock is for you right now. Screaming out the prayer. You whisper in my ear again "I'm dripping wet." Fuck. I look at you in your big beautiful eyes. Sorry, God. I take your hand and walk you down the aisle. No, the other way. Towards the back. "Come," I tell you. I find the bathroom and lock the door. You sit on the sink and look at me. "Take off your jeans," I tell you. You unbutton your pants and slide them down your legs. They stop at your boots. I kiss your lips and run my hand through your hair. Squeezing your neck. Feeling your soft boobs and hard nipples. No bra in church. You're a bad girl. I grab your hair and look at you. You open your mouth, like a seal looking for fish. I spit in your mouth and you smile. You're a good seal. A good fucking seal. I kiss your lips and squeeze your ass. It's like a fucking peach, the good juicy kind, not the old rotten ones. I want to taste how wet you are. Like Joseph never did with Mary. "Turn around," I tell you. You turn around and I admire your seal peach ass. Fuck. You're the hottest girl. "Do you like it papi?" you ask me. Fuck. You know that turns me on. "I do," I tell you, sliding down your thong. I kiss your back down to your ass. Your thong is soaked through. I slide it past your knees as I kiss your ass cheeks and spread your legs. I run my tongue and lips between your thighs and feel you dripping for me. You have the sexiest pussy. Tastes like peaches and cream. The song starts playing in my head as my tongue slides between your pussy lips and up to your clit. It's swollen and throbbing. Your pussy explodes in my mouth, like a water balloon to the face. I grab your ass as I eat you out, licking and flicking your swollen hot clit. Over and back. Driving you crazy. You are Ms. Daisy. Your ass is shaking as your pussy gets wetter and wetter, your clit gets bigger and bigger. I move my tongue between your pussy and ass. Licking your tight asshole. In God's home. I run my tongue back to your pussy again. You're moaning too loud. The nuns will hear. "Gag your mouth," I tell you. I look around and see a Bible on the toilet. "Here," I say, handing it to you. You bite down on it as my tongue goes deeper inside your tight pussy lips. Your clit is ready to cum. You moan loud into the Bible as you cum hard for me. Squirting as you cum. Fuck. You're a sexy fucker. Your ass and pussy shaking. Gripping the sink like you're going to pull it off. I stand up and slide my rock hard cock inside you. Feels like future. Your pussy is so wet and warm and tight. Like my favourite cozy sweater that's just been in the rain. You're a hot seal. I slap your ass as I fuck you deep. Pulling your hair as I think of the Lord. Spitting on your back as you start to cum again. I cum with you, shooting deep inside. I cum so hard, gripping your ass and the sink. You take out the bible and look over your shoulder at me, opening your mouth. I spit in it then you turn around and start sucking my hard, cum covered cock. Shooting again to the back of your throat as you choke and gag on it. Cum dripping down your lips and legs. You hot fucker. We kiss as we dress and smooth ourselves out. Malibu is burning. Father O' Toole is still singing. We just sinned. It's sad. So sad. But I'll donate an extra dollar and ask God to forgive. Thanks, Jesus. You're a good man. And you're the hottest fucking seal.

GOLD GIRL

It's Sunday. The Lord's day. I'm on a bus. In Knoxville. Doing shows. Touring around. Living the life. But it's too hot. Malibu is burning. And my bed is kind of slightly too small. It's sad. So sad. But you came to visit. Just flew in. You look unreal. Wearing a black Nine Inch Nails t-shirt, orange miniskirt, knee high socks and Doc Martens. Who are you? Oh, and a sun hat. You look unreal. Your skin is gold too. You're the gold girl. I want to strip you naked and bite you. I love when you're tanned. Your gold texture. Like a golden tea pot, the ones you use to make tea. "Come," I tell you, "Let's go for a walk." I take your hand and lead you off the bus. You know what we're doing. Even touching your hand gets me hard. I blame your brain. You're the most beautiful fucker I've ever seen but your brain is on another level. The finest dancer of all. The gold fucker. Your brain makes mine dance with delight. I'm hard walking the streets of Knoxville. I don't know where we're going. Need to find somewhere to fuck you and taste your gold pussy. "I went to school around here when I was young," you tell me. "Really?" "Yeah, just one year. Let's go look at it." I kiss you by the school gate. It's too hot. You're too hot. You're like a hot cup of tea that burns my mouth and ruins my day. Except you're a day maker. "Is it open?" you ask the gardener cutting the grass outside the school. "It is for you," he smiles back. Nice. He has the name tag Petey. Lovely old Indian man. You lead me by the hand and we walk inside. Looks like a Huckleberry Finn school. Christ, it's hot as fuck inside too. No AC. Those bastards. You're looking at yearbook photos on the wall. Standing on your toes. Your hair flowing.

Your skin glowing. Your skirt lifting up. Teasing me with your golden thighs. I want to kiss your legs and golden ass. You look over your shoulder at me. That one eyed look. Fucks me up. I'm going to make you cum in your old classroom. "Which room were you in?" I ask. You point to a room down the hall. I lead you inside and close the door. Seems like we're the only people here. And Petey, the gardener. I kiss you hard against the teacher's desk. Your lips are wet and juicy. Your hat falls off as we kiss harder, passion flowing, heat rising, tongues tangling. I bite your lip gently, running my hands through your hair. You're a hot fucker. You sit on the table and look at me. "Touch yourself for me," I tell you. You look at me in the eyes and lick your fingers. Spreading your legs as your skirt rises up. You're not wearing underwear. You hot fucking fucker. You start to rub your clit like a good girl. I take out my hard cock and start stroking it for you. Slowly. Both of us looking at each other. Touching ourselves. You're the best girl. You start moaning as I come closer to you. I take off your t-shirt and admire your gold boobs. They're perfect. Like you. You hot golden fucker. You're a dream. The one Martin Luther King was on about. They should have a holiday for you. I kiss your lips as we keep touching ourselves. Run my fingers over your hard nipples. You catching your breath as they get harder and harder. Your back feels so good as I pull you closer kissing you. You stroke my cock with your wet fingers. I slide my fingers inside your wet pleasure pond. It's dripping, like a leaky tap on a summer's day. Your clit is throbbing, swollen and ripe, like a mango ready to be plucked. We hear the lawn mower in the distance. Your pussy is soaked. Down your thighs. I want to taste. "Turn around," I tell you. You turn around. Like a good girl. "Bend over," I tell you. You bend over and lie face down on the table for me. I take some rope that's next to the door and tie your hands to the desk legs. You're mine now. I start to kiss your back, slowly making my way to your ass. I lift up your skirt and kiss your ass cheeks, down your thighs, the golden girl, shimmering for me, like an egg or a goose. You're a hot fucking goose. Time to pluck your gander. Your goose feathered pillow. I like your soaking pussy. Sliding my tongue inside. Your pussy gushing like a geyser. Bursting like a dam in my mouth. My tongue like a beaver. Sliding inside and out. Dancing with your pussy lips. Sliding it along your swollen clit. Hot and throbbing on my tongue. Licking your tight golden ass. The Golden Girls would be proud. You gripping the desk legs and moaning for me. Your pleasure pond dripping down your thighs. Your ass and pussy tightening and relaxing. Torturing you with my tongue. I take the metre stick next to the chalkboard. I gently tap your ass. You're tied up. I can do what I want. "You want it harder?" I ask you. You nod your head. I spank you with the stick. Across your ass and thighs. Just missing your pussy. "Harder?" "Yes, Daddy," you tell me. I spank hard. You moan and bite your lip, fighting back the pain. I spank hard again and you moan and close your eyes tighter. "Harder," you whisper. I slap you hard with the stick. You moan deep and your pussy gets even wetter. Fuck, you're a hot fucker. I walk around the desk and you start sucking my hard cock. Hands still tied to the table. Spitting on my cock. Dripping down your chin. Your red ass and thighs waiting for me. You start gagging on my cock as I fuck your mouth. My hands on your sexy tanned back. Your eyes watering. Precum shooting down your throat. I want to cum inside you. I take an apple off the table and stick it in your mouth. Sorry, teacher. You're like my hot pig on a spit. I slide my rock hard cock inside your tight soaking pussy. You feel like the ocean. Better than a sneeze. This must be what God's pussy feels like. I'm rubbing your clit and spanking your sexy ass. Like I'm riding a wild boar around the farmland. You start to cum for me, moaning loud and biting the apple. Crunching and cumming on my cock. Thick cum dripping down your legs. Petey the gardener drives by, music blaring. I pause but he doesn't look in. Listening to Closer by Nine Inch Nails. You must have inspired him. I start to fuck you like an animal again. You look over your shoulder and open your mouth. I kiss your lips and spit inside. My body on yours. Pinned against the desk. Cock deep inside you. My ponder pipe pounding your pleasure pond. I grab your ass as you start cumming again. Bodies sweating. Pussies dripping. Cocks cumming. I shoot hard inside you. We keep fucking. Kissing your sweaty lips as I cum again. I pull out and cum on your back. "Spit on me, Daddy." I spit on your back. Mixing with the cum. You're chained to the desk. Malibu is burning. I think Petey is watching us. It's sad. So sad. But fuck me pink, you are the gold girl. You deserve your own holiday. You hot pink boar.

SILK CHEETAH

It's Wednesday. My birthday. Malibu is burning. I'm 22. Kids are locked up in cages. It's sad. So sad. I'm having a dream that a hamster is chasing me around a garden. I don't know why. My teeth are falling out. I can't use my hands. I'm fully hard. It's weird. But feels amazing. Why am I hard for a hamster. Why does it feel like a cow is licking me. With the wettest tongue. Now I'm in Ireland. In the rain. In a field. With my old cow Daisy. She's licking my face. And smiling. She's a good cow. She opens her mouth to moo and says "Good morning birthday boy." What the fuck. I wake up and you're there. I'm naked. You're in your silk cheetah print lace panties. Between my legs. Sucking my rock hard cock. Oh thank God. It wasn't the hamster. Or Daisy. It was you, you hot fucker. The gold girl. Thanks, God. Giving me the slowest, wettest blowjob. Fucking Christ. A joyful birthday. The angels wept. The heavens did sing. And you did lick. I'm so fucking hard for you. Your soft lips kissing my throbbing cock. Feels like a heart pounding. Sucking the shaft as my cock heart beats harder. Slowly running your tongue down to my balls. Licking them while you stroke my cock. Staring at me in the eyes. You're a good girl. I reach for your chin to kiss me and then I realise. I'm fucking tied up. My hands and feet tied to the bed. I'm like a star, floating through the air. "You fucker," I tell you. "It's my turn to be in control," you reply smiling. You take my cock in your wet mouth again. Jesus Christ. Feels so good, like a cold shower on a hot day. Or a hot shower on a cold day. My cock is dripping from your spit. Rock hard. Dripping down my balls.

I'm fucking gone already. Ziggy Stardust floating through space. Spread out and at your mercy. You run your tongue down my cock slowly. Pressing against my balls. Sliding it along my ass. Stroking me as your tongue slides in and out. You hot fucker. You hate gluten, but love ass. You rub your finger on my asshole as you slowly suck my cock again. Licking the precum off as you slide a finger inside. Fuck. I hate this. Then love it. Is it gay? Am I George Michael? Fuck. Feels unreal. Your wet finger. Your wet mouth. My hard cock. Fucking your lips. You gag and smile at me. Tears running down your face. Happiness. The golden girl. Your eyes light up. They're the nicest eyes I've ever seen. The smartest, nicest, sexiest, hottest fucker beaming out. Your spit on your lips and my cock. Finger inside. Cock throbbing for you. Rubbing your beautiful tits on it. Sliding my cock between your boobs. Spitting on it and fucking your boobs. My legs pulling against the tied rope. My hands wanting to break free and grab you. Kiss your beautiful face. You start licking my ass again. Slowly. Softly. Harder. Running your lips and tongue up my balls. Along my cock. Slowly to the tip. Tasting the precum, like a wine connoisseur. Sipping, like it gives you life. Kissing my stomach. Slowly. Up to my chest. Kissing my nipples. I can feel your wet pussy on my leg. Your silk cheetah panties are soaked through. I'm still spread, like a plate of cheese. You're fully on top of me. Teasing me. Rubbing your wet silk panties on my hard dripping cock. Fuck, I want you so bad. You slowly kiss my lips. Going softly so I focus on kissing you. Boobs pressed against my chest. Hand on my face. Pussy teasing my cock. Kissing me like I'm about to die. I look in your eyes and kiss you back. Feeling your breath on me. Feeling your moaning on me. Feeling your body want mine as much as yours. You close your eyes as I kiss you slow. I've got you now. You're lost for me. Like a man in a maze being chased by a hamster. "Let me taste you," I tell you. You sit on me pondering. Rubbing my ponder pipe. Smiling and turning around. Your ass in my face. Pulling down your soaking panties for me. Sliding it past your knees and over your feet. Looking over your shoulder at me. In the 69 position. Your beautiful ass and perfect pleasure pond in my face. Pushing towards me as your head goes down to slowly suck my cock. I taste your pond and feel it gush. Dripping like an oily roller coaster on a wet day. Pussy soaking my mouth and chin. Fucking your juicy peach with my tongue. Sliding my lips and tongue over your ass. Your back arching as I slide inside. My hands and feet restraint. Driving me crazy. I want to touch and fuck you. Your clit in my mouth. Fucking my face as you sit on it. Slowly grinding your ass up and down as you slowly suck my hard piping ponder pipe. Playing it like a flute like you're Lizzo. Sucking and fiddling. Your pussy grinding. Your clit throbbing. Your ass cheeks shaking. I want to fuck you. "Sit on my cock," I tell you. You turn around and slide it inside straight away. You're a good girl. "Oh you fucking son of a bitch," you say, as it fully fills you up. You're a hot fucker. Riding my cock like a micromanager all over an employee. That's enough now, Trevor, I know how to do my job. Your body starts to shake. I want to make you cum. You feel fucking amazing. You golden fucker. I rip my right hand free and pull you to me. That's the bed broken, sorry, Jesus. I choke your sexy neck as you ride my hard cock. Your mouth opens and you look at me. You look gold just before you cum. "Oh fuck, Daddy," you cry as you start to cum uncontrollably. Cumming and lost. Cumming and found. Cumming and cumming again. The wettest pussy. The hardest cock. I start to cum with you, shooting deep. You ride harder. I shoot deeper. Slapping your perfect ass. I love it. Your clit throbbing on me. Your body sweaty. Looking at me with those eyes. I'm somehow only 22. Malibu is burning. The bed is broken. It's sad. But happy fucking birthday. You hot cow fucker.

SATIN SUNDAY

It's Sunday night. Our Lord is tired. Malibu is burning. I ripped my favourite t-shirt. It's sad. So sad. But we're at my show. I fell asleep on the drive. I dreamt you were kissing me and asking me to fuck you but every time I went to reach for my dick it was missing. I was a Ken doll. Then my hands disappeared. And my tongue fell off. It was great. I woke up sweating. But at the show. We're watching the acts. And you are being a flagrant disgrace. What are you wearing. A denim shirt. White bra. Thigh high black boots. How dare you. You know I'll be hard on stage now. Trying to hide my horn. Trying to hide my boner. Tucking away my ponder pipe. I like that you're a hot dresser though. You have the best outfits. I always forget because we're naked. You laugh at something a comedian says. Your eyes light up. Fuck. You're the hottest. Like global warming. It's worrisome. You catch me looking at you laughing and mouth "What?" at me. "Come," I tell you, taking your hand. I lead you out of our booth and upstairs to the balcony. No one is here. Downstairs is full. It's dark. I like it. You're mine. And now I realise you're wearing my denim shirt. Like a long dress. I kiss you against the balcony. Your wet lips. Your satin skin. You're like silk. I love kissing you. I get lost. Like I'm in a jungle without a map. You are my woods. I grab your neck as I kiss your lips. Your beautiful hair. Sex hair. Every time I touch it I want to grab and fuck you. You rub my hard ponder pipe through my jeans. It's bursting out, like it's the Hulk. Grabbing my cock as I pull open your shirt. The pearl buttons pop open. You're on the balcony. Open shirt. Thighs highs. White bra. No underwear. You hot fucking fucker. You're a good girl. You bend down and start opening my jeans. Flopping out my hard cock. Sucking me with your back against the balcony. I hear the comedian say something funny about bananas. You spitting on my cock. Sucking my balls. Stroking my ponder pipe like it's your favourite dog. Hello, Rover. Your tongue playing me like a fiddle. Touching every nerve on my cock. Lighting it up. Like you're the finest flute fiddler in town. You're a good girl. Touching yourself as you suck. Jesus. How did I get so lucky. How did we even meet. Pulling your hair back as you suck deeper. Gagging and spitting. Loving and licking. Squeezing and sucking. I want to taste you. I stand you up and kiss your lips. You're dripping wet. I turn you around and bend you over. Hands on the balcony. Me behind you. Kissing your ass. Licking your cheeks. Spanking you. They can't hear. I think. Maybe I'm deaf from booze. I had a good night last night. Woke up half blind.

Like a drunk Stevie Wonder. I spread your ass cheeks and kiss your silk satin asshole. It's so sexy. You love it licked. Like a good millennial. Teasing my tongue inside. Rubbing your clit. Running my tongue along your wet pussy. Like a wig in the rain. Soaked through. My tongue on your clit. Licking it like a stick of butter. You're my butter girl. Sexy ball. Pussy dripping in my mouth. Like a moist turkey on Christmas Day. Last Christmas playing as I pour gravy. Your ass and pussy dripping like a leaky tap. Your clit throbbing on my tongue. The crowd laughing as I rub your clit and fuck your pleasure pond with my tongue. A true dancer. The Michael Flathely of the tongue world. Feeling you cum in my mouth like a good girl. Standing up and kissing your lips. Your wet thighs and sexy eyes. You're the next level. You're heaven. You should be a Nintendo game. Sliding my cock inside your joyful pleasure pond. My cock happy as a kid on Christmas. Your warm wet pussy. My hard bulging cock. Whispering in your ear "Good girl, cum for me." You whispering back "Yes Daddy." Squeezing your neck and covering your mouth. Feeling your tight pussy squeeze and cum on my cock. Spitting in your mouth and slapping your face as the crowd below applauses. They're calling my name. Malibu is burning. I forget my new jokes. And my balls are going to be blue. It's sad. So sad. But you're going to suck my cock on the drive. Because it's Sunday. Good girl. Sorry, God.

CHERRY BOMB

It's Thursday. I'm in New York. It's raining. It's roasting. Malibu is burning. I'm wearing too heavy a jacket. I'm sweating. It's sad. So sad. But you look beautiful tonight. We are boozing. Going clubbing. I love going out with you. You're wild. And the most beautiful gem I've ever seen. Every guy stares. It's fair. Straight. Gay. Bi. They all look and want. In your black dress and black heels. Denim jacket. You look like a diamond. Dazzling the sky. You're astral. I dreamt we were fucking in the sky last night. Floating and fucking. You died during sex. I fingered your ass and you hit your head on the moon. We kept fucking. I was sad but then I woke up and you were alive. All good. Just a simple necrophilia astral projecting dream. I told you but then pretended I made it up. You looked at me weird. You grab my hand and skip us past the line. The head bouncer lifts the velvet rope. Roy, nice guy. You tell me he's a twink. I don't know what that means but I'm boozing and just nod my head and say "Yeah." This club is huge. Cherry Bomb. House music. Sweating. Packed. Dancing. Love it. We do shots and then some more. You slip molly in my mouth. Reminds me of Molly Malone back in the Ireland, selling her shekels alive alive oh. You take a shot and kiss me hard. Tequila running from your wet mouth to mine. Your wet mouth reminds me of your wet pussy, like how water reminds me of rain. We are in a dark corner by the bar making out. High and dry. Hand on your neck as I kiss your wet lips. Lifting up your dress. Feeling your pussy and clit through your black agent provocateur thong. You're soaking, like a soggy sandwich left out in a storm. I rub and tease your clit, feeling it getting bigger and bigger. I love you turned on. I love you dripping. Your pussy is like an angry river about to burst a bank. I slide my fingers inside your wet thong and tease your swollen clit. Bigger and bigger. Wetter and wetter. You're stroking my cock through my jeans. Hard as the Rock's right forearm for you. I press you against the wall and squeeze your neck. Fingering your sexy pussy. Kissing your waterfall lips. Dripping off your face. Your beautiful eyes. You smile and push me back, then do a standing splits and put your leg straight up on my shoulder. You're a fucking diamond dancer. My hot cherry bomb. "I want you to squirt for me," I whisper in your ear. "I'm going cum, Daddy," you say back. I'm rubbing your swollen hot clit and fingering your gushing geyser pussy. Tickling your g-spot. Hearing you moan louder and louder. No one cares. No one can hear. It's the Cherry Bomb. You cum and squirt on my hand. Cumming hard. Grasping me. Like a good girl. "Fuck me, Daddy," you tell me. I take you and lead you out the fire escape. We're in an alley flying off our faces. Next to the alley is a local cathedral, St. Trevor's. Lovely man by all accounts, patron saint of body dysmorphia. I lead you up the garden path to the back door of the church. Several drunk, ecstasy laden kicks and we are in the broken door. I take you to a pew and bend you over. We face the alter and smile at Jesus, then I slowly fuck you in your ass. You love it when you're on molly. You cum again for me, just as we hear police cars pull up outside. I turn you around and finish in your mouth, quickly wrapping up and making our way out the back door into the twinkling night. Malibu is burning. It's still raining. It's sad. But that was hot. My cherry bomb. And it's only a Thursday night. We were just meant to go for one. You wild diamond dancer.

SHOOTING STARS

It's Wednesday. I'm in Burlington, Vermont. Doing shows with Michael Rapaport. All sold out. Malibu is burning. His son Dean is here. The hotel messed up and only had one room for us. It's sad. So sad. There was nowhere to eat after the show so we had to buy hard boiled eggs and beef jerky from a gas station and eat them in our room. The eggs tasted like an old man's balls. That's what Michael said, anyways. He would know. You got stuck in traffic driving up from New York. It's late. 3AM. They're asleep in the bed next to me. You're going to stay the night and drive back to N.Y. tomorrow. Well worth the trip. I sneak you into the room and you crawl under my sheets. They both roll and cough but stay asleep. I think they're dying, they cough so much. Maybe the AIDS. Or the herp. Hard to tell. You take off your grey sweatpants and grey tank top. "I want to fuck you with them in the room," you whisper in my ear. You're a good girl. I like it. Your naked body on me. Just in your pink g-string. You hot fucking Victoria's Secret model. Hottest girl I've ever seen. I love touching your soft tanned skin. Your tight sexy stomach. Your perfect boobs and pert nipples. We kiss and pull our underwear off. You slide your tongue down my neck and chest. Licking my nipples. Kissing my stomach and thighs. Running your tongue slowly down my cock, like a cow licking a bull's balls from behind. I miss Daisy and Ben, my favourite cow and bull back in Ireland. You're my favourite bull ball licker now. Slobbering your tongue over my cock and balls like a drunk teen eating an ice cream cone on a wet summer's day. That used to be me in Ireland, drunk and eating ice cream in the rain, Father O'Toole watching me from around the corner. A simpler time. Your tongue slides inside my ass as you spread my legs, resting them on your back. You take my cock in your wet, joyful mouth. Feels like I'm falling into a wet bog of delight, young and carefree. You are a beautiful bog. I'm so fucking hard for you, sliding a finger in my ass as you suck my ponder pipe. Playing it like a tin whistle, your tongue like a magic dragon. I look over and see Michael staring at me, eyes wide open. The fucker is a voyeur?! No, I remember now. He sleeps with his eyes open. Dean sits up in bed next to him and screams, then lays back down and is silent. I forgot he has night terrors. I feel your pussy dripping on my leg. I love how you cum from sucking cock. Squirting on me. You hot girl. Like an old man squeezing ketchup all over his burger and fries. You lick the precum that's dripping down my shaft, then climb up me under the sheets and kiss my lips. I flip you over and kiss you hard. Squeezing your sexy neck. Your eyes smiling then closing as your lips smile wide. I squeeze harder and you gasp silently. I kiss your ear and neck, holding you down, my tongue on your nipples, hard cock teasing your dripping pleasure pond. You're sopping wet, like my cheeks when I try to put eye drops in. You open your mouth like a bird looking to be fed. I spit on your lips and go down on you. Kissing your stomach and thighs. Teasing your throbbing clit. Swollen, like an old lady's ankles after a 13 hour flight. I lick your clit slowly up and down, side to side. I hear movement in the grandads' bed next to us. I hear Michael coughing like he's about to die, then he shouts "Suck a dick!" to no one. He says that in his sleep. I think nothing of it. You're moaning too much and ass is grinding the bed as my tongue fucks your drenched pleasure pond. Your pussy is dripping like a cup I've over poured. Soaking the bed and my mouth, licking your wet, tight ass. Grinding faster as you start to cum for me. "Fuck me Father," you say into the night air. You love priests but then again, don't we all. I pop my head up and think I see Dean watching. No, he sleeps with his eyes open too. These guys are real freaks. But they're sound. You grab me and kiss me hard. I slide my cock inside and worlds collide. My mind floats to another world full of golden keys, flashing lights and shooting stars. Fucking you feels like fucking art. You're my favourite fucking bull ball licker. You claw my back as your legs wrap around me. You start to cum again. I'm brought back to this world and shoot deep inside you. I cum so fucking hard I yell out, "Suck a dick!" Jesus Christ. I cum again and feel it dripping down your thighs. I flop over on the bed and you go to suck the last drops from my cock. I look to my right by mistake and see Dean and Michael looking at me. "Are you cocksuckers done?" Michael asks us, the moonlight catching his pasty white thighs, almost blinding me. Malibu is burning. Dean has night terrors. Were they awake the whole time? It's sad. So sad. But you like being watched. You're into cucks. All good. You hot bull delight. How now, brown cow, time for some hard boiled eggs.

PURE ART

It's Friday. We're in Montreal. It was a long night. Malibu is burning. I need more sleep. It's sad. So sad. You came with us to the festival. Just For Laughs. Because you're a laugh. Rapaport and Dean love you. Don't we all. You're the fucking best. A light of delight no matter where you go. The ultimate muse. And the most beautiful feck. Who can blame us. You dancing gem. The hotel only had one room though, again. It's a disaster, in with the grandads. Michael and Dean slept in one bed and me and you in the other. They took ages to fall asleep. Eventually their sleep apnea kicked in. Both of them snoring like two trains trying to fuck in the night. Thomas the Tank and the Sad Story of Henry.

Dean was screaming again and Michael kept coughing and yelling cocksuckers. At one point you were riding my cock like a midnight express when Michael started to sleepwalk looking for the bathroom. Dean did too, naked. It was disturbing. You came on me as Michael was pissing in the wardrobe by mistake. They both went back to sleep and didn't remember a thing. It's sad they don't remember watching you cum. You're the prettiest when you're sweating and naked on me. The two pasty white sleepwalkers missed out. Rapaport had us walking around all day too. He wanted to buy some art. I can't stop thinking about you in your pink g-string as we're walking around. You have me hard all day. You should walk the Victoria's Secret show just in heels and that g-string. Even Michael said he'd buy a pink thong if you did that. You fine art. You need your own book, a coffee table ode. "People should be horny drinking coffee," Dean says at one point. I have to agree. Coffee horns are the best. The art Rapaport bought is slick. "She's my favourite artist, Sandin, come on you cocksuckers!" he kept yelling at us. We got to the studio, The Stables, before it closed but then the fucker made us carry all the art for him. What a prick. "My neck, my back, my pussy, and my crack, I pulled them all," he told us. And now we're at the show. They're doing a live podcast for a sold out crowd. I'm meant to be joining them at some point. It's just me and you to the side of the stage watching them, minding the art. They're arguing on stage, physically slapping each other. The crowd loves it. They're odd men, two grandads, but they're sound. You lean over and whisper in my ear "I'm so horny, cocksucker." Fuck. Me too. Cocksucker. We've been hanging around them too much. Your breath on my air drives me mental. You take off your leather jacket and throw it to the side. I push you against the side stage curtain and kiss your lips. Feeling your sexy legs and thighs. I love when you wear a summer dress. You rub my cock through my jeans as we kiss. I feel your warm pussy through your thong. You're wet for me. You're a good girl. "I want to suck your cock, like a good cocksucker," you tell me. Sounds like a riddle, the same one Father O' Rourke would say but about seashells. I think, can't remember. I would black out, like a 21 year old doing shots of Jäger on his birthday. You get to your knees and open my jeans. Running your tongue along my rock hard cock. The crowd is going wild, hopefully for them and they don't see us. I hear a roar as you suck my balls and spit on my cock. You start stroking and sucking, like a golfer on a bad day. I rub your boobs and play with your guard nipples, knowing you're getting wetter for me. You stand up and kiss me asking, "Feel how wet I am?" You pull off your thong and I touch your pussy. Jesus Christ, you're like summer's day in Ireland, soaking wet and warm as fuck. Your pussy explodes as I touch your clit and lips, like me as a young boy watching a Sharon Stone movie. You get back on your knees and suck me again. I feel you cumming and squirting on my shoe. My poor shoe. You cum a puddle, far better than mud. I love when you cum from sucking. The crowd are making chanting noises. I look over. Michael has Dean in a headlock but Dean has him lifted above his head carrying him around. Strong for a little man. He's only 13 too. Fair play to him. You're sliding my cock between your perfect boobs. They're the hottest. Fucking your sexy tits as you suck the top of my hard cock. You're fully naked now except for your boots. How did that happen. Fuck. You have me ready to go, like a drunk fool at a crowded bar bursting to piss. I stand you up and turn you around. Kissing your neck and back. Sweat running down you. It's hot in here, too hot, like a cup of tea with no milk. I slide my ponder pipe inside your sopping pleasure pond, feeling the wetness wilds of my life. You're cumming on my cock already, fucking you hard from behind as I choke your sexy neck. "Fuck me Daddy," I hear you yell, as the crowd continues to roar. Michael and Dean are wrestling topless on stage. A Mariah Carey song is playing. All I Want For Christmas. It's July. What the fuck is happening. I spank your ass hard every time the crowd roars, like it's your birthday. You love it. You're a good girl. I stand you up while fucking you from behind. You look over your shoulder at me. You fucker. Your eyes every time. I shoot hard inside you, cumming deep. Mariah is wailing. I'm still cumming. Suddenly there's silence. You spin around and start sucking me dry. I look up and hear my name. Michael and Dean are calling me on stage. They look over and see you sucking me. I give them the thumbs up as Michael says, "Suck a dick!" The crowd roars and I pull up my pants. I walk onstage as you're on your knees, the hottest fucker ever. Malibu is burning. It's been a long day. There's cum running down my leg. But fuck me, you're the hottest cocksucker in town.

RED THONG

It's Wednesday. I'm boozing. The Democratic debates are on. Malibu is burning. It's sad. So sad. But you look fucking hot tonight. In your black top, white jeans and black Doc Martens. You sexy fucker. With your slicked back hair. You were at a comedy show boozing. I like you boozing. Your lips look wet and your eyes light up. Some comedians went to Swingers with us. We're in a booth. You sitting next to me. My buddy chatting to me. Not realising your hand is on my cock. Rubbing me through my jeans, stroking like a villain with his cat. My ponder pipe is purring while my buddy is waffling onto me about something. I just nod and say, "mmhmmm." I look over and see your nipples are rock hard too. Popping through your top. Fuck. I want to tie you up and fuck you on the table. I wonder if they would mind? The waitress is trying to take our order but you're kissing my neck and opening my belt. I'm fully fucking hard, like trying to do a maths equation drunk. I tell the waitress "Two bowls of porridge and cups of tea." I don't know. I'm too turned on. "I need the bathroom," I tell no one in particular, like a homeless man yelling at a pole. "Me too," you tell the room, like a cow mooing in a field. Swingers is packed for a Tuesday but the bathroom is free. You follow me in and lock the door. "Excuse me, I'm trying to use the bathroom," I tell you. You're already unzipping your jeans, like a good girl. Pulling them down to show me your red thong. Fuck. I like you in a red thong. "Strip to your thong," I tell you. You do it, like a good girl. You look fucking beautiful naked, like a stunning sheep that's just been sheared. I miss my sheep back in Ireland, Tony. Great sheep, always had my back. I kiss you against the bathroom wall, feeling your sexy legs and stomach, rubbing your nipples and squeezing your neck. Your eyes shut and smile. "You like my neck, son?" you ask. "I do, mother," I tell you. Oh dear. You're my mother now. Hello Oedipus. You reach for my jeans and rip open my jeans. The belt flies off to the floor as you get to your knees and suck my balls. Spitting on my cock. Stroking it up and down. Lubing it up for your wet mouth. "I missed your cock," you tell me. We fucked two hours ago. Had a threesome with your friend Jane who's in town. Kissing her in her hotel jacuzzi. She's hot. But you're way hotter. Fuck. Your body just has me hard thinking about it all day. You hot fucker. Worse than the L.A. weather. You kiss my cock and lick the precum. A hot cherry bomb. About bite, like it's the finest fucking apple. A true Granny Smith. Tracing my cock along your lips before swallowing it full. Oh Granny. Sucking me deep, my purring ponder pipe deep in your throat. I love hearing you gag on it. I fuck your mouth, like a drunk man fucking a slow puncture. Any port in a storm. You're gagging hard as I fuck you. You take it out soaking wet, stroking it slowly, knowing I'm close to cumming. I fuck your mouth again as I shoot deep down your throat. You swallow it all like a good girl, then stand up and kiss me. I'm still rock hard. I want you to cum before we eat porridge. I take the belt and wrap it around your wrists, then tie you to the sink. You're facing the mirror as I bend you over. Sliding your red thong down your legs as I kiss your back and thighs. Running my tongue along your ass cheeks and between your wet pussy lips. You're dripping already for me, like an ice cream at the beach. I lick your wetness and slide my tongue along your throbbing clit. You moan as it slides inside, pussy gushing in my mouth, like a sycophant who won't shut up. You're wetter than a bog, gripping the sink as my tongue slides from your pussy to your ass and back again. Legs shaking as I play with your clit. Fingering you as I eat your wet asshole. Moaning way too loud as your clit gets bigger and bigger. The porridge will be ready soon. You cum in my mouth as my tongue is deep inside. Your pussy has us both soaking. I stand up and you turn your head to me. I kiss your mouth over your shoulder. "Open." You do, like a good girl. I spit inside and you put out your tongue for more. I spit again and you smile. Your ass and pussy are so fucking wet. I tighten the belt on your hands, then take my hard cock and slide inside your tight ass. Your eyes light up and mouth opens wide, silent and moaning as I fuck your tight asshole. Fucking you deeper and deeper, slowly then faster, and faster, and faster. Rubbing your clit as your legs shake again. You cum again for me, one hand choking your neck, other covering your mouth. I spank you hard and start to cum with you, deep in your ass. A knock at the door. "Everything OK?" "Yeah, thanks, dodgy stomach," I yell back. My hard cock and cum still in your ass. You're sweating and panting over the sink. I undo the belt and get dressed. You turn around and I open your mouth again. I spit inside. You smile and sit on the sink naked. Malibu is burning. The debates were brutal. And the porridge is getting cold. It's sad. But my cum is in your sexy fucking ass, and honestly, that's all that matters. It says it in the Bible. Thanks, mother. You're a fine fucking Granny.

SPORTS BRA DENIM

It's Wednesday. The weather is too hot. L.A. is roasting. Malibu is burning. Asap Rocky was found guilty. Oscar Meyer's has a new hot dog ice cream sandwich. It's sad. So sad. But at least I'm home now in the AC. I was at the gym but you kept sending me nudes. It was great. But I was so fucking hard. My cock flopping around as I tried to run on the treadmill. I couldn't do it. You wench. I liked it. I get home and you're in denim shorts and a white sports bra. Army jacket on top. You look hot as fuck. I want to bite you. "I'm nervous," you tell me. "Why?" "These interviews." You have radio and podcast interviews today for your new projects. You'll be grand. You're the smartest, hottest, most talented fucker. With the sexiest voice. They're all going to love you. "I'm so nervous and fucking horny," you tell me, kissing me hard. I take you to the bedroom and lie on the bed. You pull my shorts down and start licking my rock hard cock. It's like a man of steel around you, my cock is Clark Kent. You spit on Clark and look at me, spit hanging from your lip still. You're a sexy dancer. Like Michael Flatley in his prime, when he would dance with goats through golden gates. You wrap your tongue around my cock, like how my old cow Daisy would, while eating a strawberry or banana. She loved her bananas. And you love my cock. Deep throating like it's the last cock you'll ever see. Choking on it like it's a piece of chicken. Coming up for air like Jaws. Sucking and soaking my ponder pipe. Like a pair of runners left overnight in the rain. I'm rock hard and drenched. Your spit dripping down my balls. I love this. "I'm not as nervous now," you tell me. Your phone rings and you answer. Sitting on me as you say hello. I pull your shorts off and kiss your body. I hear you saying something like "Yeah, war is bad." I bite your neck as you speak. You moan into the phone. The radio people will love that. I bite harder and you stop talking. Grabbing your ass, you speak again to the radio people, "War is the worst." I take off your jacket and bra. Your sexy boobs and nipples in my face. I kiss your hard nipples and bite on them. You grab my hair as you start riding your clit along my cock. You're soaking wet. Naked on top of me. Throbbing clit against my roaring cock, like two lions. Your pussy is making my balls even wetter. Teasing each other. Soaking wet. Squeezing your neck and biting your nipples. Your beautiful boobs. They should win pageants. Your sexy ass. In a league of its own. You're moaning and riding your clit against my cock. Dry humping like we're 16. Me playing with your ass and pussy. Feeling you soaking on my thighs. Your clit is so swollen and hot for me. My cock is dying to be inside you. You hang up the phone with an "Oh Jesus Christ fuck me for fuck's sake." I slide inside your tight pussy. You riding me like a deranged pony. Hands slapping your ass. Nipples in mouth. Choking your sexy neck. Biting your body. Feeling you get wetter and wetter, hotter and hotter, quicker and quicker. "I'm gonna cum," you moan at me. Your phone is ringing again. It's that big podcast. I bite on your nipple as you start to cum on my cock. Cumming on me hard. Your body with mine. Spice Girl style. Like two clouds melting together. Raining down on my cock. You're moaning loud as I click answer on your phone, covering your mouth. You're breathing heavy. You can barely talk. "Say hello," I whisper in your ear, "Like a good girl." "Hi," you warble, like a new born bird. My hard cock still deep inside you. You still grinding slowly on me. You start the next interview. I slowly turn you over on your hands and knees. Looking at you in the mirror. Fucking you slowly. Doggy style. Your ass slowly backing into me. My cock getting bigger and bigger inside you. Your clit big and throbbing. Wanting to come again. You look over your shoulder at me. "Yes Daddy," you say into the phone, "I would tell my father, War is bad." I've no clue what you're on about but it makes me cum so fucking hard inside you. Dripping down your thighs. Your interviews are going well. But war is bad. Poor Asap. Poor Malibu. Poor ice cream. It's sad. So sad. But I'm still licking your pussy and clit. Watching you squirm while on the phone. You still have 9 more interviews to go. Good girl.

BLACK LOUBOUTINS

It's Friday. The world is burning. Bahamas is drowning. The Amazon is on fire. It's been like that for weeks. No one knows what to do. I posted a photo and used some hashtags. One was of my new Nike that I bought. Hopefully someone sees them and it lifts their spirits. The lungs of the world. They're dying, like my Aunt Bernie back in Ireland who died of lung cancer. She smoked 40 cigarettes a day. But apparently it was the smog that killed her. Ruined the lungs. I saw a photo of a guy wearing makeup that looked like the Amazon on fire. I clicked on a hashtag and it made me smile. He helped me. Maybe he helped the world. Malibu is burning. Again. I hit my head off a cupboard earlier making porridge. It hurt. I might have a scar. It's sad. So sad. But at least we are in L.A. At the Chateau Marmont. We came for a drink. What else could we do! We must keep our spirits high. You look fucking gorgeous. You wore your black dress and Louboutins. Hot girl summer. We have been two whures. Fucking and fucking. Sucking and licking. I blame the heat. Maybe global warming is real. Makes me sad if that's true. And so horny. The heat of it all. We are sipping on drinks, vodka for me, martini for you. We just ate some pineapple and celery slices, a nice L.A. summer meal. It's dark where we are, in the garden bar at Chateau. I wave hello at our waiter, a Brazilian boy named Giuseppe. He escaped a cartel back home and is now living his dream in L.A. serving tables. He brings another round. You take the olive in your mouth and look at me. Candle light on your face. Your hand on my cock. Rubbing it under the table. Feeling how hard I am for you, like a piece of mint candy my Nana would give me every Christmas. I miss Nana. Thinking about death makes me harder. I kiss your wet martini lips, and for a moment they remind me of my cousin Martin. He died down a well when he was fourteen. He had just gotten his first pube the day before, it was tragic. You kiss me back and my mind lights up like a firework. Feels like I'm on ayahuasca when you kiss me. The poor Shaman in the Amazon. "The world is burning," I say to your face, "So we should be fucking." You smile and grab my throbbing cock. My jeans are tight, like a fish in a squeeze. "I want your cock in my ass, papi," you whisper in my ear. Giuseppe appears at the table with another round. I wonder if he heard. He's deaf in two ears but you never know. You follow me to the bathroom and we lock the door. The warm breeze is coming in the castle window and in the distance we see smoke: Malibu. Fuck. I'm so horny for you, like a bull in heat. You get to your knees and unzip my fish ass jeans. My cock flops out, hard and ready, like it was being choked and finally got air. Gasping for your wet lips. You smile and spit on my cock, stroking it slowly. Working the head as you spit on it again. Spit dripping down to my balls. You undo your dress and it falls down your body, your beautiful boobs out for us all to see. You spit on my cock and rub it along your hard nipples. Fuck, your nipples and boobs are so perfect, like Mr. Perfect, the wrestler. He's dead too. Fuck I'm so hard. You slap my cock off your perky tits, or turkey pits as we used to say in Ireland when we were pointing out a hot girl's body, when there were people around. You rub my cock between your tassive mits then slide it into your deep wet mouth. Spit running down my balls as I fuck your mouth, like a married couple making love on their wedding night. I look out the window and see smoke in the distance. Malibu. Maybe the Amazon. All of it. So sad. So fucking hard and wet. You grab my ass as I start to cum in your mouth. Fuck me. You're unreal. I'm still rock hard. You're licking my cock and cum, keeping me hard, making me hornier. You stand up and your dress falls to the floor. Down your sexy legs. You're just in your Louis, naked and horny, like a disgraced CK. I feel your pussy and your pleasure pond drips on my fingers. You're so wet and glorious. The hottest woman I have ever seen. I wish I could write odes about you. But I can't write, I can only whistle. I briefly whistle your favourite tune in your ear, Superstitious by Steven Wonder. You smile and close your eyes, moaning and bending over the sink. Whistling always drives you crazy. I slide my hard cock inside your tight wet pussy. Fucking you must be what it's like to fuck a fish. I hope they're doing well in the Amazon. I grab your ass and fuck you from behind. Watching you in the mirror as I fuck you deeper and deeper, pussy getting wetter and wetter, like a sloppy kiss from a drunk aunt. I spank your ass hard and it rings out in the air. I spank again and hold you by your neck. Watching you in the mirror. Choking your neck as you smile and grind on me. You're a good girl. "Oh papi," you moan. "Si senior Rita," I reply. Fucking you like a good girl, forgetting where we are, your pussy eating up my cock, slapping your ass and squeezing your neck as you cum for me. You moan and scream as you cum hard, saying our Lord's name in vain. I slap you hard as you look at me in the mirror. You're drenched. "Fuck my ass, Daddy," you tell me. Oh yeah, I forgot. I slide my cock inside your ass, like how I slide inside your DMs. You light up and moan loud. My hand on your tits and clits, rubbing and fucking, you grinding and pumping, cumming again me for me, your screams bellowing out in the hot girl summer air. I cum again with you in your amazing ass. Your body is heaven. A knock at the door brings us back to where we are. It's Giuseppe, asking if everything is okay. "No," I say. "Malibu is burning. The Amazon is on fire. I just noticed I had a scar from where I hit my head on the cupboard. It's sad. So sad." But then I remembered that Giuseppe is deaf. He probably didn't hear my answer. Ah well. It's better this way.

HOT DELIGHT

Malibu is burning. It's sad. So sad. It's your birthday. So I made you a potato cake. You love potatoes. And cakes. It was a great call. I like that you ate it in one go. Wearing your jean jacket. You look hot as fuck. Your kissable face. I'm a fan. We are at your place. I kiss your lips. My hand on your neck. Your hands on my back. Your soft cheeks. My hands in your hair. You're fucking beautiful. I take your jacket off and slide your jeans down. You're in your black top. I pull it over your head and kiss you naked. Kissing your sexy body. Your hard nipples and beautiful boobs. You reach for my cock and unzip my jeans. Groping me like a priest in the night. You get on your knees and start sucking me, like a nun saying her prayers. Sister Mary O'Rourke doing her best work. I love you naked and sucking. You slap my cock off your lips and spit on it. Rubbing your clit and touching yourself as you suck. Your pussy dripping as you suck it more. Touching yourself and rubbing my cock. Standing up and bending over. You're a good girl. Taking my cock and sliding it inside your wet pussy. You're a hot fucker. Your pussy dripping wet. A hot delight. Slapping your ass as I fuck you from behind. Looking over your shoulder at me. Hands on your back. Cock deep in your wet pussy. Malibu is burning. It's your birthday. You're cumming on my cock. It's hot. I'm choking your neck as you cum. We must fuck more. It's sad. So sad. But you're the hottest fucker. I hope you know.

DONUT GIRL

It's Wednesday. We're in Chicago. Malibu is burning. Australia is gone. I'm freezing. Can't feel my face. But who needs a face. We just went donut shopping in Boys Town. It's so cold but you have me so hard all day. You sexy fucker. The gays don't seem to mind. Keep looking at my crotch while I tuck up how hard I am. The straights don't seem to notice. They're looking at you. Bending over the counter picking out a donut. I want to fuck you right here, in Giuseppe's Donut Shop For The Boys. I run my hands over your lower back. I feel you arch slightly for me. You're a good girl. You arch more and point to the donut you want. Giuseppe does his thing. You turn around and I kiss you against the counter. "Fuck me," you whisper in my ear, hand on my cock, lips on my lobe. Before we know it me, you and a bag of donuts are back in our hotel. Room door closes and we rip clothes off. It's cold so we have many layers. I struggle with a shoe while you're standing in front of me in just your black thong. Your sexy boobs. Your savage ass. Your beautiful face. I want to see you cumming for me. Like a good girl. You sit on my lap and slide your clit against my cock. I can feel how wet you are through your thong. You're like a wet willy, right in the ear. An Irish marsh in October when the bog is the most soaked. You're good bog woman. Kissing your lips and rubbing my fingers over your hard nipples. Getting them rock hard. I want you cutting ice. I grab your ass and pull you even closer to me. Your long legs wrapping around me tighter. Tear drop boobs pressed against me. Wet lips on mine. I slide your thong off and spank your ass, hard. You moan and bite your lip. I slap harder, then harder again. You're closing your eyes and moaning deeper. You love it hard. You're a good girl. I slap harder and you wince, then smile. Handprint on your red ass. I pick you up and throw you onto the bed. "Get on your hands and knees," I tell you. You do as you're told. I run my fingers along your back, teasing your lower back as you arch your ass for me. You're so fucking sexy. I spank you again. You love it. I slowly pull your wet thong down your ass and legs, kissing the back of your thighs as I go. I can feel your warm wet tight pussy from here. Lips slowly kissing. Legs starting to quiver. Spanking then kissing your ass. Running my tongue over your tight little ass. Sliding inside. Kissing your thighs and spreading your legs. Tasting your juicy peach pussy. Dripping down my chin as I run my tongue along your lips and feel your swollen clit. Throbbing as I run my tongue over and back, flicking and licking and getting you wetter and wetter. I can't believe it's not butter. You taste so fucking good. Grabbing your tits as I fuck your pussy with my tongue. In and out and in and out. Rubbing your big clit. Hearing you moan and push your ass and legs back. Holding your lower back to keep you still. Watching your legs spread wider as my tongue goes deeper. Pushing against your clit as your moans get louder. Tasting your cum in my mouth. You're a good fucking girl. You're cumming hard as I keep going with my tongue, waves and rolls and moans. I stand behind you and slide inside your drenched bog pussy. Fuck me you're golden. Tight pussy getting even tighter on my hard cock. I press on your lower back and reach for your neck with my other hand. Squeezing on it. Choking you as your head lifts up. Fucking you deeper and deeper. Wetter and wetter. Tighter and tighter. Your beautiful boobs. Your savage ass. Your sexy sexy legs. You look over your shoulder, mouth open. You want my spit and cum. I shoot hard inside you, pussy squeezing my cock. I get even harder and fuck you deeper. I pull out and you flip around, my cum covering your weapon body. You start sucking my cock and I grab your hair. Mouth open, I cum on your face and lips. Spit in your mouth and you smile. Good girl. You lick my cum off your face and tits. Rubbing your clit. Smiling. I take a chocolate donut and put it on my hard cock. You start sucking and licking. My cock and chocolate donut. You're covered in my cum and spit and chocolate. You're a beautiful bog woman. I take you to the shower and watch you get wet and glisten. You're next level. I turn you around and push you against the wall under the hot water. Sliding inside you from behind. Your wet red ass slapping off my thighs. Cock deep inside. Choking your neck with you pinned against the wall. Malibu is burning. Australia is on fire. I had to fly here on Spirit. It's sad.

So sad. But I like Chicago. Tomorrow we're going downtown to see the river. You've never seen one before. Maybe we'll find a bog too. And go back to Giuseppe's. More donuts for the boys.

QUEEN CAKE

It's Sunday. Day of our Lord. The Oscars are on. Malibu is burning. The coronavirus is running wild. It's so. So sad. But you look fucking hot today. In your ripped blue jeans and blue shirt and white heels. You hot fucker. You look like a little sailor. Not like a sailor boy. But like a sailor who would be down the docks. Doing sailor things. I just finished my gluten free vegan breakfast burrito. You're eating your bowl of porridge. You love porridge. You're a good girl. "Where are you going?" you ask me, flicking through pages of a cookbook. You want to bake me some cakes. Queen cakes and a sponge. You're a fucking queen cake and a sponge in one. "To Mass," I tell you, "Father O'Toodle is giving sermon today." He's a great man, lovely sermon, loves to sing a hymn. Hymn on. "Don't go yet," you tell me. You're horny. Porridge does that to you, it does it to us all. "Why not?" I ask. "Because I want you to fuck me before Mass," you tell me. Like a good girl. You stand up at the dining table and turn around. I fucking love your outfit. Shirt tucked in. Top two buttons unbuttoned. Jeans ripped. Your right knee showing. Stunning knee. Some guys like necks, some like collar bones. I love a stunning knee. You know it. "What underwear are you wearing?" "None," you tell me. You're a fucker. You undo your jeans and show me. "Take them off," I tell you. You do as you're told, flicking off your heels and sliding down your jeans. Standing against the table with your shirt open. I run my hand through your hair. My watch gets caught on your hair and necklace. "Sorry, hang on, wait." I struggle to untangle us. You don't care. You feel my cock through my jeans. I'm hard as a badly baked sponge. You rub it harder while unbuckling my belt, opening my zipper and flopping out my hard cock. It flops like

Freddie the whale, our favourite whale at Seaworld. We have season passes, people hate us for it but we love a good whale and seal delight. I untangle your hair as you stroke my hard sponge cock. Looking at me while stroking. My fingers running over your hard nipples. You biting on your bottom lip as I get them harder and harder. Closing your eyes as I put my hand on your neck. Head leaning back as I lightly squeeze. Breath getting heavier. Stomach tightening. Ass grinding on the table. Stroking my cock as I kiss your lips. Getting lost with you. A universal dive. You're the dream, you hot fucker. My hand runs behind your neck and hair. Kissing harder. Your legs wrapping around me. My hard cock rubbing against your swollen clit. I slide my fingers along your pussy and feel how wet. You're like a lake in May. I want to taste. You lie back on the table as I kiss your nipples and stomach. Pushing you back and spreading your legs. Your golden thighs and golden pussy. Kissing slowly. Tongue lightly on your clit. Hearing you moan. Pressing hard. Getting wetter. My tongue sliding inside. You getting louder. Your pussy dripping. Pressing and licking on your clit. Pussy gushing in my mouth. Holding you by the thighs. Ass shaking as you start to cum in my mouth. You're a good girl. I want you to taste you. I get on top of you and kiss your wet lips. My rock hard cock sliding inside your tight wet pussy. Holding you down as I go deeper. Legs wrapping around me. Hand on your neck. Choking you as you moan more and more. You're fucking beautiful. You look me in the eyes smile. "Fuck me Daddy," you say. "Okay Mummy," I think in my head. Whoops a daisy. I spank your ass cheek and flip you over. Face down on the dining room table. You'll pay for making me think that. I'm not a Mummy's boy. You look over your shoulder at me and bite on your lip. You're a hot fucking sponge. Good sailor. I hold you down by your lower back and squeeze your neck with my other hand. Fucking you deep. Pussy dripping on the table. My cock getting harder and harder inside your wet lake of May. Fuck me you're a good girl. "Fuck me Daddy," you say again. I spank your ass hard, then harder again. You love it. I spank until you're red raw. Your back sweaty. Your pussy soaked. I press hard on your ass and back as I cum inside you, cumming so fucking hard. We keep fucking and I spank more. I pull out and flip you over. You lie on the table and close your eyes and open your mouth. I cum again on your face and tits. You smile and lay there. I run my hard cock off your lips and you lick the rest of my cum off. You're a good fucking girl. The best queen cake. A lovely sailor. I look at the clock. Almost noon. I'll be late for Father O'Toodle. Malibu is burning. The virus is spreading. The Oscars are on. It's sad. So sad. But you're a good fucking girl. The finest whale I know. "Are you coming back after Mass?" you ask. You ask every time. Abandonment issues. One day I won't return. Just for a laugh. "Of course," I tell you, walking out the door. "You're a good Mummy's boy," you yell out laughing. Balls. I knew I said that out loud. Bastard. Now I'm pissed. Father O'Toodle better singing my favourite fucking hymns today. Some man.

HEAVENLY HEATHEN

It's Friday. Valentine's Day. Everyone's sad, horny, lonely, confused, in love. Malibu is burning. The Corona is on fire. My stomach has a virus. It's sad. So sad. But Jesus you look savage. In your black and strawberry dress. The one that's black and has strawberries on it. One of my favourites. You're at the dining room table. Working on your website. Reading a book. Battlefield Earth. An L. Ron Hubbard classic. You'll be joining Scientology soon, I just know it. Can't wait to join a cult. You're a hot cult. You look at me and smile "Where are you going?" "To buy more porridge," I tell you. Your smile disappears. I've been feeding you porridge all morning. It's romantic, the most romantic Irish dish. But you're sick of it. You're full to the brim. "Just eat some of my banana bread," you tell me, "It's healthy." "Really?" I ask. "Yeah, doesn't have sugar or any of that shit," you say. You're so gruff with your words. I like it. Your cat Tabby meows at me. It just stares. Reminds me of my Aunt Tabby. I think she was autistic. I think your cat is too. Just stares but has a lazy eye. "I'll be back soon," I tell you. "No, come with me." Fair. I follow you to the bedroom. "I bought some toys last night." You love getting drunk with your buddies and going to sex shops, it's the best. You're a horny bowl of porridge. I'm getting hard just thinking about it. You get onto the bed on your hands and knees, the cow pose. Our favourite. "Look in the back," you tell me. I reach for the sex shop bag as you pull your dress up. Your beautiful ass and red thong in the air. Jesus you're a hot cow. With the hottest legs. I spank your ass and you smile. Reminds me of a grey sky on a summer's day in Ireland. Fucking beautiful. I spank again and you moan. Sounds like a little moo. You're a good cow. I open the bag and laugh. It's just a potato and a strawberry. My favourite sex toys. "Take your dress off," I tell you. You do as you're told. I like that about you. Ever since I met you in a car park drunk dancing to some Euro trash house music you've been a good laugh. Just a pity you can't rollerblade. Your only downfall really. That and you break a glass and cut yourself every time you make a toast. Okay, you have a lot of flaws. But you're like an ice cream on a rainy day. Still refreshing. I pull your red Santa thong down your legs. Rub your ass cheeks, then spank harder and harder. You moan louder and louder. The neighbours will hear. Ginnie and Lily, the old lesbian couple next door. I don't need to hear them yelling "Come join us instead, sweetie," while we fuck. It's potato time. I put it in your mouth. You look at me with your beautiful eyes. You love a good potato. I get behind you on the bed. You've a sexy back. I run my fingers down it, massaging you to your lower back and ass. Looking at you looking at me in the mirror next to the bed. You're beautiful, like seeing a sunset above the clouds. I spank your ass hard again and watch you bite down on the potato. I kiss your lower back and feel how wet you are. Your pussy is glistening. Clit getting bigger and bigger as I kiss your thighs and ass cheeks. You moan louder into the potato. I slide the strawberry inside your wet pussy. It's dripping wet. I spread your ass cheeks and slowly slide it inside your ass. Your perfect peach and strawberry ass. Even better than your healthy banana bread. I taste your wet pussy and rub your swollen clit. Hand on your back as I slide my tongue inside deeper and deeper. Feeling your hot clit and hearing your muffled moans louder and louder. I run my tongue along your swollen clit and feel you starting to gush in my mouth. Arms and knees shaking, barely holding you up. Stomach and body tensing as you start to cum. Strawberry dripping out your ass. Cumming hard as I keep licking your wet pleasure pond. You're a good girl. "Phock meh," I hear you muffle into the potato. I slide my hard cock inside your tight, wet pussy. Jesus Christ you feel like heaven. You're a heavenly heathen. I push your body down to the bed. Face in the pillow. Strawberry peach ass in the air. My hand on your lower back. Your favourite. I squeeze your neck as I fuck you deeper. Hair on your face. Pussy dripping on my cock. Sliding in and out, wetter and wetter, harder and harder. Clit throbbing and hot. Biting on the potato as I spank you hard. Your ass is red raw, just like how jolly old Saint Valentine would want it. I start to cum hard as you bite through the potato. Shooting deep inside you. Your ass fully clenching the strawberry. Juice and cum and potato everywhere. You turn around and start sucking me. Fuck me you're a beauty. I cum in your mouth again. You're a horny girl. Makes me even harnier. Malibu is burning. My stomach is on fire. Corona is dead. Tammy has been staring at me the whole time. It's sad. So sad. But you're the best Valentine's ever. A true heavenly heathen. There's a knock at the door. It's Ginnie and Lily. Tut, I knew it.

FLORAL GIRL

It's Saturday. It's too bright. I'm hungover. Malibu is burning. China has a virus. Bernie Sanders just won in Nevada. It's sad. So sad. But you have me up and out of the house. You wanted to go to the cinema. Driving down the PCH. Through Malibu. Sad to see the fires raging. Like my stomach. For some reason I drank Whiteclaw last night. It's all they had. Horrible jungle juice, as you call it. You look beautiful in your white floral dress. Your boobs spilling out. Your thighs showing. Your hand on my crotch as we're driving. Rubbing my cock through my jeans. I think you're horny. "I'm horny," you tell me. I knew it. I always have a great sense of things. Father Bernard used to tell me that growing up in the parish back in Ireland. It was like every time I sensed he was luring me down the back fields to show me a cow, I knew he was just trying to fiddle me and I would run away. Fun times. You have my jeans undone and my cock is out. Slowly stroking me. Looking at me as I drive. I'm so fucking hard. Can barely drive. I just want you sitting on it. "Suck it," I tell you. "Yes Daddy," you reply. Good girl. Your lips on my cock. Tongue running over it. Licking the precum. Lips sucking it off. Spitting on the head as your tongue licks up and down the shaft. Getting harder and harder for you. Pulling up your dress and rubbing your ass as you swallow my cock. Hearing you gag on it like a good girl. Like how Father Bernard wishes he could've, the cheeky bastard. I feel in the bog one time when I was running away. Fleeing and I fell. Oh how we laughed. My cock is rock hard and dripping in your spit. I'm pulling at your black lace underwear. You sexy fucker. Feeling how wet your pussy is for me. Like a sock that stepped in a puddle. Hate that. Love your pleasure pond. Fuck. I'm so close already. You look at me and smile. You know I'm close. We're stopped at a light. You reach up and kiss me. My hand running through your hair. Pulling you back and looking into your beautiful eyes. You're intense. I love it. Like a fire at the circus. You rub my balls and start sucking again. I cum hard in your mouth. Feeling you swallow as I shoot again. Fuck. I want you on me. I pull in as you keep sucking. You pull your panties down and sit on my lap. Sliding my cock inside your tight drenched pussy. Hand on your neck as you ride on my hard cock. I'm so fucking hard for you. You sexy fucker. Choking your neck. Like an empty Whiteclaw. You smile and close your eyes. "Fuck me Daddy." You're a good girl. Ass riding up and down. Breathing heavy. My cock deep inside. You grinding slowly. Clit swollen and throbbing. Rubbing and feeling you breathe sharper. Choking you harder. Pussy clenching on my cock. Cumming for me like a good girl. You're banging the roof as you cum. Fuck me. You're unreal. Kissing your sexy lips. Choking tighter. Cumming more on my cock. "Cum for me Daddy," you say. Grabbing your ass as I cum again. Shooting deep inside you. Your head hitting the window. Your hard nipples in my mouth. You look at me and smile. "Can I have a chocolate chip cookie?" you ask. Malibu is burning. Bernie won. We're going to the cinema. We'll be late. It's sad. So sad. But you can have a cookie. You're a good girl.

GLORIOUS FUCKER

It's Sunday. The day of our Lord. Tyson Fury. Wilder lost. Malibu is burning. I lost $100 somewhere. It's sad. So sad. But at least Father Tony O'Rourke gave a lovely sermon at Mass this morn. Something about helping the less fortunate. Leprosy victims I think. I can't remember. You were too distracting. Dressed in your hiking outfit. All black. Tight pants. Ready to go. I was mesmerised by your face. Your lips. Your beautiful fucking eyes. Intense. I love looking in them when we fuck. You had me hard at Mass. I think Father Tony knew. Gave me some extra wine at communion. Asked me to go to confession later. I declined. The dirty whure. I was turned on the whole hike after too. Your sister is in town. Showing her around. Mass. Hike. Now we're going to Venice for the day. She's picking us up soon. Came home to shower. I have you naked. You have me hard. You're sitting on the bed, running your tongue along my cock. Down slowly to my balls. Sucking on them as you look at me in the eye. Intense girl. Spitting on my cock and stroking it. Sliding it between your beautiful boobs. Rubbing the head on your hard nipples. You're a good girl. "Spread your legs," I tell you. You do it. I feel your wet pussy and swollen clit. Feels like a swell in the waves. Hot and throbbing. Pussy wet and dripping. You deep throat my cock and I hear you gag. Coming up for air, spit and precum running down your lips and chin. You suck again, my cock getting even harder in your mouth. I want to taste you. You lie back on the bed and spread your legs. "Flip over," I tell you. You lie face down on the bed. Stomach flat and ass up. Legs spread and pussy waiting for me. I spank your ass and massage your back. My cock teasing your pussy from behind. Sliding along your wet lips as I massage harder. Running my hands in your hair. Tight on your neck. Squeezing. Pressing on your back. Pushing your lower back down. Your ass pushing up for my cock. You want it. I want you to cum first. I kiss your ass cheeks and run my tongue between. Your lips spreading as I slide it inside. Gushing in my mouth, like a burst water balloon hitting my dumb head. Your clit is hot and swollen for me. Running my tongue along it as I hear you moan. Same noise Father Tony made as I slurped down the wine. I slide my tongue inside you again. Spreading your ass cheeks as I slide it from your pussy to your tight ass. Teasing you and feeling you go wild. Rubbing your clit and feeling you clench and grind your ass even more. Face down as you moan into the bed. Ass grinding as I feel you getting close to cumming. Grabbing on the bedsheets as your body tightens. Pussy dripping in my mouth. Tongue pressing on your clit. You moan loud as you cum for me. Sunday's finest. Grabbing at the pillow as your leg shakes. You want me inside you. I slide my cock inside your soaking pussy. Your ass bouncing back at me, like a wave of glory flowing and flowing. Rippling as I fuck you deeper and deeper. Hitting your ass hard as we fuck. Pushing you into the bed even more. Hand on your lower back. Body dominating yours. Spanking you hard like a good girl. You're biting the bedsheet. "Fuck me Daddy." I fuck you harder. You love it on your stomach. You want my cum inside you. I grab your ass as I shoot hard. Fuck me pink. You feel fucking amazing, like being drunk during the day. I shoot again as you whimper "I'm coming, I'm coming." Fuck me, your pussy gets tighter and wetter. Sweet Jesus, you're the dream. Like a waterfall on my cock. I pull out and lay next to you. You smile and look at me. My cum dripping out of your pussy. Malibu is burning. Your phone is ringing. Your sister. We're going to be late. Your pet peeve. I think Father Tony might have stolen my money. It's sad. So sad. But fuck me pink, you're a glorious fucker.

ART WOMAN

It's Tuesday. Super. Love a nice Tuesday. Although. Malibu is burning. Nashville is windy. The Democrats are fighting. Bernie. Biden. Sanders. Which of the three will win? It's so. So sad. But I walk into the apartment and see you on the kitchen floor. You're naked. Ass in the air. Like a lovely place to park my bike. You're painting. Oh yeah. Tuesday night painting. Your favourite. I remember when I first met you, you told me you had a secret. I wondered if it was that you're racist. Alas, nay. You just love to paint naked in the kitchen. Awful secret. You should have taken that to the grave. Like my uncle Tony. Oh the secrets he has. Behind the shed. With the sheep. In the dark. Bad man. Say no more. "Hi," you say, wiggling your ass. "I'm painting." "I can see," I tell you. Sometimes I wonder how dumb you know I am. "Join me?" Of course. You're the most turned on when you're painting. I'm the most turned on watching you paint. I love seeing your talent. You talented bastard. You're covered in orange and red and pink paint. You look like art. I strip naked and join you in the kitchen. I love you in orange. Reminds me of the troubles in Northern Ireland. Trouble turns me on. "What are you pain-" Before I can finish you've turned around and started kissing my half hard cock. Fuck. You're a good girl. Your tongue on my balls. Lips kissing along the shaft. Getting me rock hard then slowly sucking me. Looking at me as you spit on my cock. Stroking it slowly as you suck my balls. Tongue going further towards my ass. Spitting again and sucking my cock deep. Gagging it on, like a cleaner smelling a pub bathroom after a night out. I'm so fucking hard for you. You dip your hand in paint and slap my ass. You fucker. My turn. I pull you to your feet and look at your eyes. They're like the ocean and a black hole in one. I look at your beautiful mouth. I like your mouth. Pulling you closer. Your mouth facing mine, like two ports gone wrong. I feel your ass and spank you. Grab your hair and look you in the eyes. You open your mouth and I spit in it. Good girl. I feel your clit. It's throbbing. Your pussy is like a river bank ready to burst. The poor villagers. I want to taste. I move you to the kitchen, placing your hands on the counter and spreading your legs. I spank your sexy ass and squeeze your neck. Your head moves back as you moan. You love it. Feeling your pussy get wetter. Hand on your lower back. Spreading your ass. Kissing your cheeks. On my knees. Tongue on your thighs. Finger on your clit. Throbbing. Rubbing. Soaking. Moaning. Wetter and wetter as my mouth teases your pussy. Clit getting bigger. Pussy getting wetter. My tongue sliding between your lips. Your pussy gushing, like an over eager aunt on a wedding day. I'm rubbing your ass and clit as I lick your tight pussy. Reminds me of a fish's ass. We should have sushi later. You're moaning louder as my tongue fucks your pleasure pond. Like Uncle Tony and the sheep. Loving it. Your thighs shake and I lick you deeper. Clit swollen. Ass clenching. Starting to cum in my mouth. You're a good girl. You're grabbing the counter and cabinet as you cum hard. Your leg lifts and foot lands in paint. You kick me in the chest by mistake. Bad girl. I've an orange foot print. Nice. You look at me and laugh. You fucker. I dip my hand in red paint and spank your ass. You moan and bite your lip. Other hand in orange paint. Spank the other cheek even harder. You love it. Like a good sheep. "Get on your hands and knees," I tell you. "Like Nelly the Elephant?" you ask. "Like Nelly the Elephant," I tell you. That was your favourite childhood story. You love painting elephants. You're a good Nelly. You get on the kitchen floor. Ass in the air. I take the orange paint and pour it on your back. You moan as it touches your skin. Like when a creep touches my hand. You look hot covered in paint. You are fucking art. "We should have sushi after," I tell you. "Yes Daddy," you reply. You're ridiculous. I'm trying to give up meat for Lent. I asked if you would and you said no, you're too much of a meat lover. "I crave steak in the AM," you said at one point. You hot nut. I squeeze your neck and slide my hard cock inside your soaking pussy. It's like a sock that stepped in a puddle. You're a good elephant. Slapping your ass off my thighs as I fuck you deeper and deeper. Your boobs hanging like two beautiful melons. Hard nipples like an advanced maths exam. I spank your pink ass cheek and paint splatters. Your pussy gets tighter as you get wetter. My cock harder and deeper inside you. Two ports in the night. Red ass cheek hard. Clit swollen. Dominating your fucking weapon body. On you. Body weight. Fucking you deep. You fucking art woman. "You're a good Nelly," I yell out. Your legs shake as you cum again. You love elephants. Fuck I want to cover you. I flip you over on your back. You take my cock and stroke me as I shoot hard. Cumming all over your body and face. You love it. Smiling. Like a good girl. Malibu is burning. It's Tuesday. Super. Poor Warren. Poor Nashville. It's sad. So sad. But we gave up religion for Lent. Just Uncle Tony. You piece of fucking art.

DENIM FUCKER

Fuck. It's Saturday. The day of the Lord. I think. Not sure. Still drunk. Malibu is burning. L.A. is raining. The coronavirus. Rampant. Can't stop touching my face. It's sad. So sad. You were at a cake baking class. Finally home. I woke up in a heap. So harny. I'm a harny boy. You made a pavlova and seventeen queen cakes. You did well. I'm on the couch. You walk in. Leather jacket. Black jeans. White bodysuit. You're a hot fucker. You have the cakes. "Want a cake?" you ask me. "No," I tell you. I want you. You put the cakes on the counter and come to the couch. I kiss your fine face. You're golden. The hottest fucker. Your body against mine. Hand in your hair. Pulling you closer by the neck. I take your jacket off. You look at me and unzip your pants. Kissing your soft lips. Like two tulips on your face. You are tulip face. What Father Timmy used to say when he rubbed my tummy. I can't remember being sick but he would make me better. Like a young deer on a spring day. Leaping for dear life. Like my penis. Hard as a rock. Curious and dancing. You stroking it through my jeans. Stripped down to your white bodysuit. Your hard nipples teasing me, like Aunt Nicole, horny at a Christmas party. Unbuckling my belt and pants. I want to make you buckle. Your hand on my cock. Stroking. Grabbing my balls. Kissing your lips. Undressing you. Pulling your bodysuit down. Off your shoulders. Kissing your lips, then your neck. Bodysuit pulled down your body. Down your sexy legs. Just naked in your underwear. A denim thong. Bold choice. That's why you're the best. You enjoy a nice denim, like John Travolta, being a 40-year-old teen in Grease. You take my t-shirt off and pull my jeans down. I slide your denim thong off, like a child sliding down a slide. I love you naked. Hard nipples and wet pussy. Pushing my cock against you, like a true creep. Your mouth wanting my kiss. Grabbing your ass to pull you tighter. Spreading your legs. I know you're dripping. Soaked pussy, like a puddle in May. The wettest month. I squeeze your neck as we kiss. Slide my fingers between your clit and lips. You're throbbing. Soaked and wanting. My cock hard as a bag of nails, which are renowned for being hard. Stroking me as I rub your clit, throbbing and throbbing. I turn you around and push you onto the couch. Your hands on the back. Bent over. A good girl. Fingering your tight wet pussy. Kissing your neck. Hand on your back. Lips on your skin. Hearing you moan. Your sexy lips. Your sexy skin. You beautiful fucker. Kissing your lower back. Your sexy ass. Each cheek. Fingering your throbbing pussy. Licking your sexy ass. Like a tight knot. Kissing and licking. I'm a sailor boy. Your ass is the knot. Fingering your sexy pussy. My cock hard as Christmas. Spreading your cheeks. My tongue going deeper. Fingering and feeling your ass shake. I want you to cum. Eating you out and fingering deep. Your clit thick on me. Fingering deep as you start to cum in my mouth. Eating your sexy pussy from behind. Your knees buckling as you cum in my mouth. Looking over your shoulder at me. Mouth open. Eyes alight. Sexy fucker. You tulip. Hand on your ass as you cum in my mouth. Spreading your legs as I slide my hard cock inside. Your lips spreading. Like the corona. Can't stop touching my face. Filling up your pussy. Hand in your hair as I fuck you deep. Slapping your ass as you scream Aye Papi. Italian, I think. "Aye Papito," I yell back. Rubbing your clit as I fuck you deep. I grab your stomach as you cum again, you're a good fucking girl. I cum with you, shooting hard inside you. You're beautiful. My hard cock deep inside. Body against yours. I pull out and shoot on the back of your leg. A wasted dream. Your poor thigh. You swivel and suck. Taking my cum in your mouth. Malibu. Burning. Denim thong. I ripped it. Corona. Everywhere. It's sad. So sad. But you cumming makes it all worth while. You're the worst. You sent me a meme of a black man's penis. But the best. It made me laugh. You hot denim fucker. Farewell, my corona.

HOT LEOPARD FUCKER

It's Sunday. Day 1. Quarantine. Day of our Lord. Malibu is burning. Toilet paper is gone. Corona is everywhere. It's sad. So sad. Even Mass was light this morning. No hymns or holding hands. Me heart ached. Poor old creepy Jimmy was gutted he couldn't hold my hand for Our Father. Sad. So sad. But I get home and you're just in your thong. Putting away the groceries. You chose food over God. You're a bad girl. We have porridge galore. We'll be grand. "I got us soap," you tell me. "Oh lovely," I reply, touching my face 79 times. It's an illness, I can't stop. Only when I touch you. That's been our plan to survive it all. Keep on fucking. My hands are all over my face again. "We should fuck," I tell you. "I'm so fucking horny," you reply. You always get like this around pandemics. A horny dancer. I love it. "Come," I tell you, leading you to the bedroom. You grab the sanitiser. You're a good girl. Like that movie where the bees kill Macaulay Culkin. Poor fella. Maybe he deserved it. The bees are sound. I kiss your lips as I push you against the wall. Your hands undoing my belt and jeans. Taking off my t-shirt as I look at your sexy face. Your lips wet and dripping. They're so beautiful. You're like a wet potato, my favourite. Not a fan of the flowery ones, they're like an old vagina. I told you that once and you told me you didn't get it, too Irish. But it's true. "Google it," I told you, you slapped me, it was hot. We are both nearly naked. You stroking my cock through my strawberry themed boxers. Me rubbing your hard nipples and feeling your clit through your leopard thong. Jesus you're sexy. You're dripping already. I slap your ass and pull you closer. Kissing your sexy mouth, the opposite of a trout. My cock is bursting out of my boxers for you. You slide them down and flop it out. Looking at me while you stroke. Me pulling your thong down with one hand, other on your neck. Keeping you against the wall. Keeping you a good girl. Your pussy is drenched. It'll catch a death of cold if you were outside. But we're not, we're inside, fucking like quarantined rabbits. I kiss your lips and your neck. Run my tongue over your hard nipples, biting on them softly. Grabbing your hips as I kiss your stomach and thighs. On my knees. Spreading your legs. Running my tongue over your clit. Sliding it slowly between your lips, like a magician slipping a card back into the deck. Your pussy is a deck of cards, you magic leopard fucker. My tongue is deep inside, hearing you moan, grabbing my hair as I tease your clit. Slowly flicking it back and forth, up and down, in and out. Your pussy getting wetter and wetter, like a muddy trail in the Wicklow mountains. I almost died there once. Porridge poisoning. Your thighs are wet from how turned on you are. I flip you around and kiss your ass cheeks. Grab the sanitiser and wipe you down. Eating you out from behind. Rubbing your clit as I fuck your pussy with my tongue. Licking your tight ass and tasting your soaked pleasure pond. Throbbing clit getting bigger and bigger. Moaning with your face against the wall. You're a good girl. I grab your ass cheeks as you start to cum. Moaning hard and thighs shaking. Stomach pressing against the wall, touching your clit as I fuck your pussy. I stand up and slide my cock inside you. Sweet Jesus, you feel fucking amazing, like a Sunday roast on a wet June day. You hot potato. Your pussy is wetter than a bowl of gravy. I slap your ass and grab your neck from behind. Pulling you up. Cock deeper inside you. Pressed against the wall. Our sanitised bodies against each other. Your pussy dripping on us. Down your thighs. All over my cock. Turning your face and opening your mouth. I kiss you hard then spit inside. If we die, we die together. If you die and I don't, ah well, we tried. I choke you more and feel your pussy tightening on my cock. "Cum for me," I tell you. "Fuck me Daddy," you moan. Cumming on my cock, like the hottest fucker you are. Malibu is burning. I'm cumming with you. In your pussy. Shooting on your back. You flipping around and on your knees. All over your lips and face. There's no toilet paper. Corona is all over. It's sad. So sad. But we have porridge. So that's grand. We're grand. Don't worry, we'll be grand. You hot leopard delight.

DYSTOPIAN TULIP

It's Day 5. I think. No longer know what day anymore. Just the numbers. Quarantine life. I like it. You don't. Malibu is burning. The world is over. Celebrities are singing "Imagine". People are doing Instagram Live non stop. The neighbour put a reindeer antler wig on their cat and it ran off crying It's sad. So sad. But it's making me harny. And you even harnier. It's only been five days. But we can't stop fucking. And pumping. And pumping some more. Work is over. Life is gone. We start afresh. Like two tulips. A dystopian time. A dystopian future. Indoors and hoarding milk. We just finished working out in the dining room. I need to sweat. You need sex. It's great. Your body is the ultimate weapon. Your toned back and unreal ass. All those squats. With your flat stomach and perfect boobs. I thought we'd kill each other locked up. I almost kicked you out. But you showed me a meme in the nick of time. The naked black man sitting on a bed. With the huge dick. Who would've thought, a big black penis saved us. We laughed and hugged and fucked on the kitchen table. After I looked him up to thank him. His name is Wood, a gay porn star. But he's dead now. Died in 2011. So sad. So so. We're considering porn. The new world. You'll sell feet photos. I'll sell bed pumping videos. Me having sex with my bed, like we used to do in Ireland. I'll kiss the pillow. It's niche but I'm hopeful. We can make money. We have enough to survive another 23 months but the panic is kicking in. Maybe we just start tomorrow. "I'm so fucking horny," you tell me, peeling off your work out clothes. Harny. I think in my head. "Me too," I say out loud. You turn around, topless and place your hands on the bathroom sink. "Is my ass still good?" you ask, peeling off your gym shorts. "You hot fucker," I tell you, spanking your right cheek. We sanitised, it's okay. "Harder," you tell me. I slap harder, letting it ring out. Birds scatter in the air nearby. A bat in China perks its ears. It was a good slap. "Harder, Daddy," you say. I whack your ass hard with my palm, stinging us both. Your ass clenches and I see you biting your lip in the mirror, moaning and breathing hard. Your legs look amazing, long as a July 4th weekend. Paddy's Day was two days ago but it feels like two years. Everything is long. Your fucking legs, you Daddy Long Legs. I spank hard again and you spread your legs for me. Your pussy is glistening, like a wet marsh. Your boobs look amazing in the mirror. I play with your hard nipples, my hard cock pressed against your ass cheeks from behind. Hand on your neck, choking slightly. Kissing your shoulders and ear. Nipples harder and harder. Cock pressing deeper and deeper. Your boobs look amazing in quarantine, like two laden jugs, a farmer's wife. They remind me of an Enid Blyton book, The Famous Five. When they were stuck on the marsh and the farmer's wife gave them jugs of milk to save them, you know the one. Your body relaxed, your pussy wetter, like a mellow marsh. Almost a marshmallow but not quite. You hot fucking Enid Blyton. Feeling your wet pussy lips. Thank God your name isn't Brenda, that would be sad, so sad. I feel your back and ass again. Choking your neck tighter. Nipples and boobs high in the air, like two balloons that got away. You're a fucking weapon. I kiss your back and ass, sliding my tongue between your tight ass. Hearing you moan as I toy with it. Feeling your cheeks clench and loosen as my tongue slides inside. Rubbing your clit as I fuck you with it. Feeling it get bigger and bigger, pussy wetter and wetter, like a blossoming tulip in the November rain. I flip you around and you sit on the sink, legs on my shoulders, face between your thighs. Your pussy waterfalling into my mouth, like a waterfall and whatnot. My tongue on your clit, feeling it throb. Fingers in your pussy, feeling it drip. Your hands on my hair, face in your pleasure pond, tongue between your lips, sliding inside. Gushing in my mouth, like a geyser gone too soon. You moaning and muttering and breathing heavy, speaking in riddles and rhymes. Making no sense, like a geezer going to the moon. I lick hard on your clit and you start to cum. Stomach sucking in, pussy pushing in my face, ass clenching and pulling my hair. "My poor hair," I say into your pussy, tongue darting on your clit, like Bambi on ice. You cum even harder, squirting and yelling "Oh fuck, oh fuck, fuck me Daddy." There's no one else in the room so I presume you're talking to me. I stand up and kiss your lips and mouth. Your cum on my lips. Your cum on your chin. My hand pulling your hair. You breathing deeper. Hotter. Harnier. Grabbing and stroking my cock. Sliding it inside your soaking pussy, like a slippery McDonald's floor. Fuck me pink, you feel fucking amazing, like your own bed after a 14-hour flight. You feel better than any bed I've pumped, and I've pumped a lot. Your fingers in my mouth. Sucking on your finger and thumb. Choking your neck. Just your thumb in my mouth. Moaning as I suck it. Fingers on my jaw and chin. Holding my face. Ass and pussy clenching on my hard cock deep inside. Cumming again for me like a good girl. Squirting on my cock. Grabbing you tighter as I start to cum with you. Shooting deep and getting harder. Body dominating your weapon. Choking your neck tighter. Fucking you, slapping your ass, having the time of our quarantine lives. You pull my cock out and get to your knees. Cum shooting on your tulip face. Covering you, a cum mask. You smile and look up at me. Looks like my face after I used a Hanacure™ face mask last week. I looked stunning after it. You look savage covered in my cum. I pull your hair and you look at me and smile. Malibu is burning. The world is over. Wood is dead. It's sad. So sad. But at least we keep fucking, like two harny fucks.

TOILET QUEEN

It's someday. I don't even know. My legs have gone numb. From sitting down and reading. Malibu is burning. The streets are dead. Viruses are in the air. It's sad. So sad. But we heard CVS has toilet paper. So now we're on a mission. Driving in silence. You're worried. You've been drinking too much coffee. I'm more worried. Too much Guinness and coffee. My stomach is like the neverending marsh in the neverending story. The poor horse. My poor vowels. I haven't even been horny. It's been the worst. Fucking Rona. Ya dirty whure. You look hot as fuck too. In your red pants and black hoodie. Hoodie covered in cat hair. You hot fucker. My ponder pipe has been in self isolation. The stress of it all. I need toilet paper. You feel my cock through my grey sweatpants. Nothing. We both look out the window and say nothing. A tear in our eyes. Maybe it's the virus. Maybe it's not. I haven't been this soft since Father Terrence walked in on me in the school showers naked. Claimed he got lost. That silly old man, he seemed to always get lost and find me in the shower. Then he'd sit down and tell me a story, as to keep my company. I could never remember the stories because my memory has it black out, but I'm sure they were a hoot. He's dead now. Like my penis. Ah well. Driving down Beverly. "Whatever happened to your friend Bayley?" I ask you. She wanted to have threesomes. Love pegging, apparently. "She died on a cruise ship," you tell me. Sad. Same as Father Terrence. He loved cruising. We get to CVS and it's surprisingly empty. People have given up hope. You sprint inside. You're very horny. You need my penis to come back alive. Alas, the toilet paper aisle is empty. You break down. Fall to your knees. Weeping. Security guard looks at me, an older man named Leroy. He nods his head towards the ice cream part of the fridge section. That sneaky bastard. A 6 pack of toilet paper. My bowels leap for joy. Jesus Christ. My dick. It's back. God is a she. She has returned. I slip the man $20, but throwing it from 6 feet away. He smiles and nods his head. I grab and pay. "Look, you fucker!" I yell at you down the aisle. You raise your head, tears gushing, then splutter and smile. "But, but how?"

you say, laugh crying. "Shhh. Let's go." We sprint to the car. It's dead outside. Lock the doors. Fuck me. We did it. I no longer have to use your hand. You unzip your hoodie and sit on my lap. Your ass beeps the horn. Pants come down as you keep beeping the horn. Horny fucker. You kiss my lips and rip my pants down, then pause. Afraid. What if. Please God. You grab my dick and start crying and smiling, laughing and kissing, horny and wet. It's hard. My dick is rock fucking hard. It's a whatever holiday is closest miracle! I pull your sweatpants down and rip your thong off. You're fucking soaking. Like a dam running wild. A river running loose. A fox bounding across a dewy field. You are the fox. I am the hound. You're fucking beautiful. I'm fucking horny. I squeeze your neck for joy. You close your eyes and smile. You thought it was over. You were in the desert. Like Jesus. Looking for water. Looking for wine. Squeezing tighter. Rubbing your clit. It's throbbing. A swollen little fucker. Your pussy, the wettest it's been. A flock of geese flying through a grey cloud. I finger your pussy as you moan loudly. Hand on my hair. Hand banging the roof. You're going fucking wild. Like a freshman on molly. Time of your life. "Fuck me," you say, like a demon possessed. I grab your neck. You slide my rock hard cock inside. You gasp for air, like a shot of Adrenalin to the heart. You're back. He's back. You're shaking as my cock slides deeper inside. Moaning loud. Security guard pops his head out the door to see what's going on. I pull you tighter and place my hand over your mouth. You grinding on my cock. I can feel you cumming already. Grinding and rubbing your swollen clit. I rip open the toilet paper and shove one in your mouth. You bite down like a good girl. That's your roll now. Grabbing your hips as you grind harder and deeper on my cock. Hard nipple in my mouth. Grabbing your tits. Choking your neck. You're fucking soaking on me. Pussy dripping. I rub your clit and you start to cum harder. "Oh baby, no, keep going." Oh fuck. You start squirting on me. You horny fucker. Soaking my thighs and stomach. Cock drenched. I love it. Spitting out the toilet roll and kissing me hard. I slap your ass and grab your hips. You squirt more as I start to cum with you. Shooting deep inside your pleasure pond. Ponder pipe piping.

Cumming hard with you. Sucking on my thumb as I shoot again. Malibu is burning. My dick was numb. The virus was winning. It's sad. So sad. But we're back. We're horny. And we have toilet paper. You toilet queen. Poor Bayley though, so sad she died. At least she died pegging, doing what she loved. Lucky girl.

HARNY BROKEN GIRL

It's Sunday. The day of our Lord. I only know because Mass has been cancelled. It hurt me heart. Malibu is burning. Our hands aren't clean. The virus is spreading. It's sad. So sad. And you haven't been able to have an orgasm in days. The stress. The world. The ending. It's all coming shattering down. Even the post office is closed. We went to mail your Dad his laptop charger. No joy. You're drunk. Espresso martinis. The day is all over the place. I tried to go to the Farmer's Market but it was too busy. So sad. I couldn't risk it. Me heart. Me lungs. Me thirst for tulips and turnips. You know I love my Sunday turnips. But alas. No joy. Driving home in silence. You sipping on a to-go cup. Me longing for turnip and leek soup. I love a good leek. Sister Francine would make it for me when I was young. Sitting in the convent kitchen watching her stir the pot. Asking if I wanted to lick the spoon. Then lick her fingers. Then showing me touch her nipples with my fingers. So long. So hard. So harny. Such lovely soup. I look over and you're reading your book. "Women," it's called. About lesbians. You look like a lesbian today. Wearing your pink velvet tracksuit. You hot fucker. This is madness. We must fuck. I want to make you cum. It's the only way we can survive. I sped up and get us home. You trudge inside. You need another martini. "Look at me," I tell you. You turn around and I kiss your lips. They're soft and supple and wet. I love kissing booze off your lips. I pull away and your head floats back. Eyes open and you smile. "What was that for?" you ask. "For fucking you," I tell you. I'm getting you out of your lull. I need you dancing. I kiss you again, harder against the kitchen counter.

Unzip your pink velvet sweatsuit top and slide it off. You're not wearing a bra. Just your beautiful tits free for the world. You're the sexiest fucker. I remember the first time I saw you. Naked in a room full of horns. An art exhibit of some sort. Made me horny. So fucking harny. And now you're just a harny broken girl. A toy with a broken wheel. Time to fix you. I kiss your lips and run my hand through your hair. Feel your boobs and hard nipples. Feel you breathing heavy as I kiss your neck. Your hand reaching for my cock. Hard in my pants. Stroking it. Teasing. Making me the harniest boy. Moaning in your ear. You on the counter. Me between your legs. Our hands on our bodies. T-shirt coming off. My hand on your neck. Your nails in my back. Your pants pulled off. You and your wet black thong. You're a good girl. I'm going to make you cum. Until we're both fucked and dumb. "Come," I tell you, taking you by the hand to the bedroom. You lay on the bed as I pull your thong off. Down your sexy legs. Kissing your nipples and stomach. Teasing your thighs and legs. Kissing your stunning knees. You hot fucker. You lay on the bed as I look at you. Taking off my jeans. Loving your body. You're a piece of art. You're a piece of work too when you're in a mood but fuck me pink. If you're not the hottest fucker ever. I get on top of you naked. Kissing your lips. My rock hard cock between your legs. Rubbing along your clit. Against your thighs. Rubbing it along your lips and feeling how wet you are. You've been too broken to cum with me. I kiss your lips and you pull me closer. Your tongue on my tongue. You lick my teeth and smile. You love that, you hot fuck. I lick you back and you lick again. Your pussy getting wetter, I can feel it on my balls. Resting on your wet lips. The cock on your throbbing clit. Looking at you. Your face. Your fucking eyes. My hand on your neck. You raising your chin. Squeezing gently on it. You sucking on my fingers. Holding your chin as you suck. Playing with your nipples. You're pinned against the bed. You're mine. I spread your legs and slide a finger inside. You close your eyes and moan, just like Sister Francine when I would squeeze her nipples. Lovely woman. Your pussy is soaking, your perfect lips tight and throbbing. My cock rubbing against your clit. Like two lesbians scissoring. Two fingers inside. Deeper and moving up. Beckoning for you to cum for me. You bite your lip and breathe deeper. Eyes closing. Nipples harder. Clit throbbing. You're soaking wet on my hand. Like an over eager fucker who used all the Purell. My hand is drenched. "Fuck me," you whisper. "No," I tell you. "Not until you cum." You breathe deep and sound pissed. I love it. Getter wetter and wetter as I finger you deeper. Biting on your lip harder, breathing through your nose, feet clenching. "Please fuck me," you say. "No. Beg." "Please fuck me, please." You really want me inside you. Not until you cum. I open your underwear drawer next to the bed. Take out your vibrator. I squeeze your neck gently as I turn it on. Resting it on your thigh. Closer to your clit. Vibrating. Not touching your pussy. Teasing it. Fingering you while the vibrator moves closer to your throbbing clit. "Fuck me, fuck me, fuck me," you plead again. "No." I hold you by the neck and watch your face as I finger you. Soaking wet. Legs clenching. You're getting closer. I can feel it. Vibrator teasing the fuck out of me. Like me with Father Gerry when I needed money for sweets. Flash him some thigh. Sweets for days. I grab your thigh. Hold the vibrator close to your clit. Your breathing deeper and deeper. Heavier and heavier. Legs starting to shake. I almost touch your clit with it then just tease your ass instead. Rubbing it along the outside. Along your lips. Hovering on your clit. It's begging. You're begging. Hand on your neck. Watching your face. "Please," you whimper. I rub your clit with the vibrator and watch you smile and clench and cry and cum. You hot fucker. Stomach tensing and pussy flowing. Ass in the air and nails on my back. Fingering you and pressing the vibrator harder on your clit. Cumming hard for me. Like a good girl. "Please fuck me," you gasp, almost crying. I slide my hard cock inside your tight soaked tulip of a pussy. Who needs Jesus when I have your pussy. Sorry God. You feel fucking unreal, like a hot bowl of turnips on a cold March day. You wrap your legs around me and my cock goes even deeper. You feel like fucking heaven, better than touching my face. You suck on my fingers as I fuck you hard. Your soaked pussy on me, the sheets, the air, everywhere. You grab my ass as I start to cum hard. Shooting inside and seeing the Lord. Sweet Jesus. You open your mouth and look at me. You're a good girl. I pull out and cum on your body. Leek soup shooting through the air. On your beautiful boobs and chin and face and mouth. You're a sexy fucking fucker. Jesus Christ. Malibu is burning. The virus is winning. Our hands aren't clean. But fuck me pink. I love when you cum. Christ, I'm fucked and dumb.

HOT WELLY

It's Friday. I think. Who knows. It's all a blur. Three weeks in. Malibu is burning. The streets are empty. The grocery stores are full. It's a mess. A coughing sneezing spitting mess. It's sad. So sad. I spent an hour in line to buy milk at Trader Joe's. A guy tried to fight me because he thought I had a cold. He was wearing a welding mask and about 65. He was too old to fight. A woman with a stick hit him instead. I bought a bright red hoodie while lining up. $200 from a diner. I'm losing it. I'll buy a yellow t-shirt tomorrow. Just because. I get home with the milk and see you're in a mood. You've been locked up for 20 days. You're horny and bored and angry and hot. All the time. It's fucking amazing and not. But I like it. "What milk did you get?" you ask. "Almond." "I said oatmeal." "You said almond." "Did you not check your texts?" you ask. You're fucking ready to go. I can tell. Like a horny priest on his first day on Sunday school. You're about to explode. "I didn't get any texts," I tell you, "I was busy with an old man and a red hoodie." You look at me confused. Standing in the kitchen in your pink hoodie and black booty shorts. Hair tied up. Like laces on a shoe. Or a welly. You hot welly. "You're a hot welly," I tell you. "What the fuck is a welly?" I kiss your angry confused lips. They're wet and soft. I know your pussy is dripping wet already. You're kissing me back. "Farmer welly shoes," I tell you. Can't remember the American name. Google it. Your hoodie comes off over your head. Your glorious boobs in the daylight. Jesus you're a hot fucker. I'm going to make

you cum like a good girl. You slide your shorts down your legs.
I take my top off and lead you to the bedroom. Your vibrator
is on the bed. You good girl. I kiss your lips as as you undo my
pants. Pulling my hard cock out of my boxers, like a trout in the
night. Stroking my cock as I tell you you're a good girl. Hand
on your neck. Squeezing lightly. Looking in your eyes. Your
fingers playing with my precum already. My fingers rubbing
your clit. Watching your face as you breathe heavier. Deeper.
Moaning softly. Biting on your lip. Clit throbbing. Getting more
swollen. Kissing your lips softly. Squeezing tighter. Feeling
your dripping wet pussy. You're a good girl. I love you dripping.
Like a wet towel being let out to dry. You hot welly. I feel your
hard nipples and grab on your tits. You look at me as I feel them
getting harder and harder. My cock harder and harder. Stroking
slowly as I slide fingers inside your tight wet pussy. It's like the
gap in the car between the seat and the seat belt thing, the tight
part, you know the one. Like the gap behind the church and the
back wall where Father Tim would play hide-and-go-seek with
us. We could barely squeeze through because he would always
be so close behind us. I loved that game. I love your pussy. I lay
you on the bed and kiss your lips. Your pussy soaking for me. I
turn on your vibrator. Even the sound drives you crazy when I'm
there. I lay next to you and slide my cock inside you. Holding the
vibrator against your clit. Right hand on your neck as I squeeze
while we kiss. You breathing deep and moaning. My cock sliding
deeper inside. Your clit swollen and ass quivering. Fuck you feel
fucking amazing. "You're a good girl," I tell you. "Promise?" you
ask, looking me in the eye. I choke your neck and kiss you hard.
"You're a good fucking girl," I tell you, feeling you cumming for
me. Your legs locking and pussy squeezing on my cock. Kissing
you hard as you cum. Fuck you feel too good. I shoot deep inside
you, cumming hard with you. Fuck me. Grabbing your tits as I
shoot again. Kissing you harder. Laying you fully on your back
and getting on top. Pulling out my cock and shooting on your
body. You rubbing my cum on your tits. "Open your mouth," I
tell you. You do as you're told. I look at your pussy and watch
my cum dripping out. Looks so fucking good, like a waterfall

on a winter's day. Like a mentos in a bottle of can. Streaming down your legs. I rub my finger along your pussy lips. You open your mouth wider and I let you suck my cum off. You suck hard while looking at me. I'm fully hard still. You hot fucker. I rub your pussy again. You open your mouth and suck my fingers dry. You cum guzzling slut. You're a good girl. I love it. I scoop more cum and you suck again. I'm so hard for you. While you're sucking I slide my cock inside your soaking pussy. It feels like heaven. Like the end of quarantine. Like we're finally fucking free. Malibu is burning. The streets are dying. I got the wrong milk. It's sad. So sad. But you're a good girl. You fucking hot welly.

RAY OF LIGHT

It's Sunday. The Lord's Day. No virus can stop the big man. Malibu is burning. The corona is spreading. The droplets are everywhere. It's sad. So sad. But I still went to Mass. I was safe there, in a room with a hundred other people and God. He looked after us. We all blew the virus away, huffing and puffing in Jesus' name. I think that'll work better than any medication. Father Jimmy was so nice too, offered to help me blow in his private quarters afterwards. Sweet man. I had to make it to the farmer's market though before it closed. It was packed. I need to get your bananas and oranges. Your Sunday treat. You were worried I shouldn't go but it was a wet market, the corona is just a dry cough. Plus it was the weekend and sunny outside, so it was fine. Quarantine is mostly for the week. And the weak. I get back to the abode laden with fruit. More laden that my swollen balls. All the blowing and shaking and touching at Mass got me harny. Thinking of you before I left. In the kitchen stirring a pot of porridge on the stove. You're a good girl. A hot housewife. A true Virgin Mary. You told me you were dripping wet before I left. Begged me not to leave before I fucked you. But I didn't have time. God was waiting. I told you when I came home. You said you would wait like a good girl. Except now I hear moaning. And your sweatpants are on the kitchen floor. You little fucker. I walk to the bedroom and watch you as you're touching yourself. Ceding on the bed. Black lace thong around your angles. Nipples hard as a riddle. Bursting through your grey tank top. Rubbing your swollen clit. Moaning and stomach going up and down. Tits rolling like a man on molly. A beautiful wave. But you're a bad fucking girl. You don't even hear me. I step inside and you look at me. "I'm sorry," is all you say. "You're a bad girl," I tell you. "I told you to wait." "I'm sorry, I tried," you tell me. You're in trouble. You know it. "Stand up," I tell you. You do as you're told. "Pull your thong up." You do it. They're soaking wet. I'm going to tease you now until you're begging. Your nipples are so fucking hard. You're a beautiful fucker. You look so sorry and horny. I love it. I feel your nipples and pull on them. Pinching softly until I see your face wince. Watching you biting your lip. Kissing and licking your left nipple. Holding your hands behind your back handcuffed. Hard nipple in my mouth. Hearing you breathe deeper. Biting softly on it. Kissing your body. Your collar bone. Your neck. Holding you by the neck. Pinching your right nipple. Your eyes closing as you moan softly. Breathing out your nose as you bite on your lip. I move you up against the wall, facing it. I want to feel your wet pussy from behind. I take your hand and guide it to my cock. You stroke it through my jeans. Harder and harder. I pull your tongue tight on you. Between your perfect ass cheeks. You're soaking wet, like a ferret caught in a summer rain. Pulling your thong between your lips. Tight on your swollen clit. "Open my jeans." You do as you're told, deftly with one hand, like a one handed man opening a can. Taking my rock hard cock out and stroking as I move your thong between your pussy lips. You're a good girl again. Getting wetter and wetter, like a melting glacier in these troubling times. "Please fuck me," you whisper. "Are you a good girl?" I ask. "I am Daddy," you tell me. "Not yet." You breathe deeper and get even wetter. My hand is getting closer and closer to touching your clit and fingering your drenched pussy. Teasing you with your lace thong. Last time I say you wear it was when your friend Karen was over and I watched you two fuck. Going down on each other as I stroked my cock. Looking at me while your tongue was on her clit. Karen cumming hard as you stared me down. You hot fucker. My fingers now close to finally touching your clit. Thinking about it. You deserve to cum. Stroking my cock as I press you against the wall. Pulling your thong to the side. Feeling your swollen clit, bigger than a swollen lip after a fight. Your pussy starts gushing as I rub back and forth on your clit. You start cumming hard. Ass clenching and face against the wall. You're a beautiful fuck, like a ray of light brought to life. I slide two fingers inside your Notre Dame and the floodgates explode. Gushing and soaking. You're like a wet ride. I lift you up and slide inside. I haven't felt lips this wet since Sister Ann taught me how to kiss for my Holy Communion. She tasted like a jar of jam and cigarettes. Still love the taste to this day. My cock is lost inside your tight wet pussy, like me looking for my car at a Target parking lot. I hold you by your neck against the wall, squeezing and slapping your ass. You start cumming on my cock again. Fuck me, you're a good fucking girl. You look around and I kiss your lips. You're whimpering and moaning. I press you against the wall as I cum inside you deep. Your glorious pussy squeezing on my cock. Filling it with treasure. A Goonies cave of gold. My wet hard cock is so full for you. I pull out and back away. You turn around and get on your knees. Opening your mouth. I grab your hair as I cum on your face and tits. Shooting on your lips, like Bishop Lucey would cover me in the body of Christ. "Forgive me Father," you say on your knees. This makes me cum again, the passion and love of Christ. I shoot on your body and you rub your hard nipples. Malibu is burning. The virus is winning. Your oranges and apples. It's sad. So sad. But we're going to fuck all day and forget about it. Maybe invite Karen over. If you're a good girl. You smile and lick your lips, swallowing my cum. "Want some porridge?" you ask me. Fuck me pink. You are a ray of light.

ANAL DELIGHT

It's Monday. And overcast. I think it was raining. We're all locked inside. Malibu is burning. No one knows what the fuck is going on. It's sad. So sad. And it's fucking Monday. Laundry day. The worst. We're all so harny. At least it's your turn to do the laundry. I wish I had a dungeon to lock you in and do the laundry all the time. My secret wish. Nothing would turn me on more. Instead you're in the bedroom. So sad. We need a dungeon. You're in a white shirt with lace underwear. Pulled high around your waist. Fuck me pink. Why are you looking so hot. I want to fuck you on the pile of sheets and socks. You dirty laundry fucker. You seem to read my mind and put on white socks. Your outfit is complete. And now I'm hard as fuck watching you from the living room. Haven't been so turned on by socks since I walked in on my Uncle Toby making love to our old neighbour Bert when I was a wee lad. Aunt Sally wasn't happy with that one. The two old lads fucking each other in the ass. Now I want to fuck your ass. Thanks, Toby. You catch me staring at you. "What?" "Nothing." "Do you want to fuck my ass?" you ask, back to me, looking over your shoulder. "I'm going to," I tell you. You smile and look away, climbing onto the bed slowly, like a goat up a tree. I watch as you open the side table drawer and take out your toys. Turning around to face me, your vibrator and anal beads between your legs. I come to the bed and watch you slide your white panties off. Legs spread. Pussy wet. Fully glistening. You're a beautiful fuck. You should be down the dungeon. A sexy troll. I walk to the bed looking for my favourite socks. Okay, they're to the side, they're safe. Good. Standing by the bed and opening my zipper as you smile and pull my cock out of my pants. Jeans and boxers to the floor as you take me in your mouth. Getting harder and harder as you spit and suck. Opening your shirt and feeling your nipples get harder for me. You're looking at yourself in the mirror at the end of the bed as you suck my cock. Good girl. I like you watching. Gets me harder. Pinching your nipples as you spit on my cock and suck my balls. Shoving my cock deep down your throat. Hearing you gag on it then pausing and

161

sucking more. You're a good girl, I love fucking your mouth. Spit dripping down your chin. My hand rubbing your clit. Feeling it get bigger for me. Spreading your legs and rubbing your wet lips. You're soaked. Dripping down to your ass. I slide two fingers inside and feel you breathing heavier on my cock. Sucking like a lollipop. Lil Wayne would be proud, clapping from the balcony. That song is in my head now. Humming while you suck. You love when I hum, especially while fucking you. Almost as much as that time I sang George Michael while fucking your ass. I can be your father figure. Reminds me of Father Liam and the promises he would make me in the back of his white van. He has the nicest sweets. Almost as sweet as your wet pussy. I'm fingering as you drip on my hand. Sucking as my palm presses on your clit. I rub your ass with your pussy juice, lubing your tight hole. Massaging and fingering slowly. Feeling you get wetter and wetter, like a sad woman's cheeks as she sits in the shower. We all love a weep. Your ass wants to wail. I spit on my hand as grab your anal beads. They're like Ferrero Rocher chocolates. Reminds me of Christmas parties back in Ireland. Of how we all loved those chocolate balls. Pure oral joy. Pure anal joy for you. Holding your hair as I slide a bead inside. Ass grinding and pussy pushing in the air as I slide another in. Panting on my cock as the third slides up. Sucking on my cock like it's giving you life. You're a good girl. An anal queen. Watching yourself in the mirror sucking and squeezing your ass cheeks. Squeezing your neck. Your body is ready to explode. Rubbing your clit. My cock on your lips. Not touching your face. You don't like it. Only cum. A weird dilemma. But I like it. I turn on your vibrator and tease your lips. Your clit is yearning. Begging. It wants to be sucked. I want you to squirt for me. I press the vibrator against your clit as you start moaning louder and louder. You can barely suck. Breath deeper and deeper. Panting. Stomach up and down. Grabbing your tits. Squeezing your ass as I push a fourth inside. You're ready to cum. I guide your hand to the vibrator. "Watch yourself," I tell you. You do as you're told. Looking at yourself in the mirror as you press the vibrator on your clit. Knees bent and legs spread. Closing and shutting. Moaning and writhing.

My hand on your neck choking. Eyes closing. "Watch yourself," I tell you again. You look in the mirror as you start to cum. Good girl. Cumming hard as your legs shake. Pressing harder on your clit as you start to squirt. So fucking hot. Soaking and squirting, like my childhood days in the field. All over the clean socks and sheets. "Good girl," I tell you, as your mouth reaches and sucks my cock. Holes fully plugged. I want that ass. Slowly pulling the beads out of your ass. Getting on top of the bed as I look you in the eye. My hard wet cock going slowly inside your tight ass. Vibrator on your clit. Thighs soaked. Pussy drenched. Neck choked. You grab my neck as my cock slides deeper inside. Choking me back as I feel your tight ass up. Like a dungeon filled with light. Or a foot, filling a sock. It's too much but you love it. Cumming again as we get lost. Squirting on me as I get deeper in you. Choking. Kissing. Cumming with you hard. Lost in laundry and anal delight. Pulling out and stroking as you open your mouth. Shooting all over your face, rejuvenating you like a Hanacure™ face mask. You smile and lick your lips. Spent on the laundry pile. You're a dirty fucking sock. Malibu is burning. I forget what day it is. And now you must do the laundry again. It's sad. So sad. But fuck you're a joy of anal delight. Thanks, Toby.

MONDAY ROAST

It's Monday. Still. Somehow. When will the days end? Malibu is burning. The prison life burns on. You squirted all over the laundry. It's sad. So sad. But you washed it again. Because you're a good girl. We showered and fucked again. Your body soapy and wet. Glistening and tan. Holding the shower head as I fucked you hard against the wall. Hot water on our backs. Your nails digging into me. My hand choking you as I watched your face. Looking you in the eye as you came again for me. Fucking deep inside your tight wet pussy as your cum flooded down me. It was fucking hot. And then I ate porridge as you did the laundry. Hot dungeon girl. I'm watching you again. Folding socks. Fuck. You look stupidly hot. Like a dunce who was beautiful. A salmon gone wrong. A ship that sailed too soon. You're in your black shorts and white tee. I'm still in a towel. A lazy fuck. With a lazy boner. Just popped up watching you. Your fucking back turns me on. Lean and toned. I want you pressed down face into the bed. You catch me looking and see I'm hard. "Again?" "Again. I know. Fuck you. It's your fault." You move the clothes off the bed as I walk in. I kiss your lips and pull you close. Your nipples hard against my body. Hand in your hair, on your neck, ripping off your top. You beautiful fuck. I love your body. Kissing and licking your nipples. Harder in my mouth. Your hand in my hair as I kiss your stomach. Pulling your shorts with my teeth. Pushing you to sit on the bed. Pulling your shorts down your beautiful long legs. Reminds me of my third cousin Tony's legs. He was quite a dancer. A young Flatley in heyday. Leaping through the air like a rabbit gone wrong. Your lean dancing legs turn me on like a song. You lie back on the bed as I crawl on top of you. My knees on your arms. Your mouth open. My cock slapping against your lips. "Are you going to be a good girl?" I ask. You nod with pleading eyes. Desperate to please me and suck my cock. Teasing it along your lips. "Look at yourself in the mirror," I tell you. You turn and look. Fuck, you look so good. Like a Sunday roast after a long sermon at Mass. But it's Monday, you Monday roast. Your tongue licking the head of my cock. Pulling and pinching your nipples as I kneel up. "I want it Daddy," you plead again, my fingers rubbing your clit and pussy lips. Your hands and arms pinned down. My cock teasing your beautiful lips. Rubbing it along your cheeks as I feel your tight pleasure pond get wetter and wetter. Eyes closing when I touch your clit. Lips reaching for my cock. I want to taste your pussy. I kiss your lips and pull back. You open your mouth as I spit inside. You're a good girl. I move my tongue down your body. Biting softly on your nipples. Holding your hands down. My lips on your stomach. My hot breath on your clit. Teasing. Breathing. Tormenting. Breathing on your lips. Slightly touching with my tongue. Kissing slowly on your thighs. The top of your ass cheeks. Spreading your legs. My tongue by your ass. Teasing your wet pussy. Getting closer and closer. Slower and slower. Hearing you moan as you feel my breath on your clit. Goosebumps on your thighs. Ass quivering. Legs shaking. My tongue close to sliding between your pussy lips. Holding down your knees. Pinned to the bottom. Slipping my tongue inside your soaked pleasure pond, like a priest in the night around the rear and in the back door. Father Gary, a devilish man. My tongue deep in your tight pussy. You shaking in pure delight. You're a good girl for me. I like it. Fucking your pussy. Sucking your clit. I want you to squirt again for me. My mouth soaked in your pussy juice. Tongue flicking back and forth on your swollen clit. Pressing on it. Fingering you. Sliding a finger in your ass. Your body lifting off the bed. Pinning you down again by the knees. Moaning louder and louder as I press and suck on your clit. Shaking and grabbing my head as you cum like a thief in the night. Exploding on me, like the Kool-Aid cartoon bursting through a wall. Squirting as I keep licking. Getting on top of you and flipping you over. Face in the pillow as I spank your ass hard. Sliding my cock inside your golden egg pussy. Feels like a Chinese New Year. Jesus Christ you're hot as fuck. My body dominating yours. Spanking hard as I fuck you deeper and deeper. "Are you my good girl?" I ask in your ear. "I am Daddy, I am." you whimper back. "Are you my good girl?" I ask again, spanking your ass hard. Red raw. "Yes Daddy," you cry out. My hard cock deep in your tight pussy. Spanking harder. Hair in your face. Biting the pillow. A little princess. Spanking you hard. Holding you down on your lower back. Squeezing your neck. Shooting deep inside you as we cum together. Fuck me you're amazing. I'm cumming like a firework. Lost in your bliss. Lying on your body as I slowly fuck you. Pulling out as you turn around. Watching yourself in the mirror. "Can I touch myself?" you ask. "You can. You're my good girl." You rub your clit and watch yourself in the mirror. You cum again, squirting on my hard cock. I stroke my cock and shoot on your body and tits. Looking at you in the mirror. Malibu is burning. We're all prisoners and housewives. The bed is soaked. But you're a hot fucking piece of work. A salmon gone wrong.

DECADENT GIRL

It's Tuesday. The worst day. It has no feel. And it's raining. Malibu is burning. USA is strong but the virus is stronger. It's sad. So sad. Everyone is in a fog. Dull brains. Dim light. A retired lighthouse or a ship smuggling drugs. Lost and aimless. I went for a drive to clear my mind. Just driving around the block singing George Michael at the top of my lungs. It's the only thing keeping me sane. But singing George makes me harny. And the rain? It's the worst. And I saw a guy littering while crossing the street. Now I'm angry and harny. Driving home. Singing "Everything She Wants." The best. Reminds me of you. You hot feck. I walk in and you're standing by the dining room table. Fuck. You're in all black. My favourite. Black crop top and black leggings. That means black thong too. I need you naked. "What are you doing?" I ask. "Crocheting," you tell me, not looking. You're knitting nipple hats. Your new quarantine thing. It makes no sense. And that's okay. Sometimes I've no fucking clue what you're doing or why. I like it. The vodka and tequila bottles are both out. Oh no. Oh yes. Fuck me. This will be fun. You're at your harniest. "What are you drinking?" I ask. "Vodka and raspberry. And tequila on the side." I come behind you and wince at your nipple hat. "Do you like it?" you say, holding it up. "Nay," I tell you "But keep going." You look over your shoulder pretending to be pissed, like a drunk ferret stopped at a DUI check point. You're a hot fucking ferret. I kiss your lips. I love your boozed up lips. Wet and horny. We're going to be naked soon. You know it. "Tell me you like it," you pout. "No," I reply, "But I like you." You smile and feel my cock as I grab your ass. Pushing into me as I get harder against you, kissing your wet vodka lips. They remind me of Aunt Trudy's, oh how she would drink gin and pay me £5 to let her kiss me. Now those were the days. The dining table is covered in your stuff. Ferrero Rocher chocolates. Yarn. Coconut oil. Nipple hats. It's a mess. "Why is it so messy?" I ask you. "I'm sorry," you say. "You're a bad girl. You need to be punished." I turn you around and grab you by the hair. Sitting on the table as I tease your lips. "Take your leggings off," I tell you. You do as you're told. Good girl. You slide them down. Standing in your black top and thong. Fuck, you're beautiful. I feel your pussy, it's soaked. I love your wet pussy lips pushing through your thong. I kiss you again as you slide your thong down your legs. Naked from the waist down. Your weapon body peaking out under your crop top. Your long legs waiting to be told what to do. Your ass afraid to sit on the table or stand up. Push getting wetter and wetter. "Are you going to be a good girl?" I ask you. You nod your head, mouth slightly open, starting to breathe deeper. "Turn around." You turn around as I spread your legs. Hands on the table. My cock out of my jeans as I slap it against your ass. Your pussy is dripping. I feel your clit and slap your lips softly. You moan as your wet lips smack. Sounds like a seal hitting the ground. Like an old man sucking on a toffee. I take a Ferrero Rocher and unwrap it. "You're not allowed to ruin this, okay?" You nod your head. You're being a good girl. I slide the chocolate ball inside your pussy. You keep your legs spread. You're afraid. You're not going to ruin it. Your pussy is soaking. Gushing as I slide the decadent chocolate inside. You decadent fuck. Moaning and nervous. "Don't fucking ruin it." "I won't Daddy," you reply. You know what's coming. You love random anal on a table. It's your favourite. I take the coconut oil and rub it on your ass hole. Between your sexy cheeks. You've the Marilyn Monroe of asses. Whatever the fuck. You're getting wetter and wetter as I lube your tight ass. My cock pressing against you. Sliding inside your tight pretty hole. Slowly. Inch by inch. Slowly inside. Your pussy nervous. Soaking. Dripping wet. Grabbing your nipples with me as I slide fully inside. Standing up as I kiss your lips. Bite your ear. Hand on your neck as I squeeze tighter. Grabbing your hair from behind as I fuck your perfect ass. Slapping off my thighs as you go faster. Breathing hard. Pussy shaking. Ferrero Rocher.

Clit throbbing. Pulling you close. Slapping your ass cheek hard. Harder. Ringing out. Pulling your hair like a wild horse. Slapping and spanking like a bad girl. You're a good girl. Arching your back. Slapping you hard again. Pulling your hair and hand on your swollen wet clit. You're so fucking wet. You moan loud and legs shake as you start to cum hard. The first wave hitting as your stomach tenses and ass squeezes. You're lost. I love it. A pigeon in the woods. A deer at sea. Me drunk at a bar. Blind and loving it. Choking your neck as you cum again. "You're a good girl," I whisper in your ear, cock buried deep in your tight delight of an ass. A donkey in song. Moaning out as you slide up and down. Rubbing your clit. Feeling your pussy. Wet as Aunt Trudy at Christmas. Paying me to dance and dominate. My cock getting harder and harder. Your ass wetter and wetter. Feeling your decadent pussy. Chocolate intact. Fuck. You cum again for me, squeezing the chocolate. You hot fuck. I'm going to cum. I shoot deep inside, like a rock down a well. Fuck me pink. You wear pink on Wednesdays. You're a good girl. I shoot again and pull out. I cum on your back and ass. You lay face down on the table panting. Smiling. Happy. I cum again on your back as you smile. Malibu is burning. It's Tuesday. I hate litter. But you're a good girl. Almost. Next time. You open your mouth and I slide the chocolate in. You hot fucker. You turn around and look at me, hard and still harny. You rub your clit looking at me. Getting harder. You're still dripping wet. Rubbing. Harder. Harder. Looking at me as you cum again, squirting on the ground. Good girl. You decadent fucker.

FROG FUCKER

It's Wednesday. I think. Whomst knows. Not I. At least it's not raining. But still. Maybe that's better. Malibu is burning. Bernie is out. Some army guys were at the shop acting as security when I went to buy milk. I forgot my mask. It's sad. So sad. But you're in your green hoodie and purple thong so I don't care. It's my favourite outfit of yours. You look like Kermit and Miss Piggy's love child. You hot frog. With your hot pig ass. I love a little pig ass. It's what Farmer Seanie Beag used to call me growing up. "Let me slap that little pig ass," he would say as we ran through the dark barn, laughing. I was only 7. He was 42. Fun times. You were up early for a conference call. Some sort of Zoom. And now you're boozing. It's barely noon. So I'm guessing the call went well. Your friend Karen is over. She's boozing too. We all got tested. Corona free. So sad. I would've enjoyed the drama of it all. Maybe I'll lie. Get some sympathy. Set up a GoFund me. Buy myself some T-shirts. While I'm daydreaming you and Karen are whispering on the couch. Drinking Bailey martinis. Fuck, you're beautiful. You hot toned porky pig. Karen is in her black thong and t-shirt for some reason. I feel a shift in the air, like when a priest enters the confessional. Something's about to go down. On cue you and Karen start making out. Hot fuckers. I'm standing with my pint of milk, watching and getting hard. Your soft lips caressing. Dancing on each other. Tongues touching and lips pressing, like two ballerinas. I'm fully turned on, like an oven on Christmas morn. Just, you're hot. You look at me and laugh. Karen throws me daggers. I walk to the bedroom and put my milk on the bedside table. You and Karen follow me in, leading her in by the hand. We stand by the bed for one awkward moment, then I kiss your Karen kissed lips. You taste so fucking good, like a bowl of soup just before you die. You're my death's row porridge. The thought of porridge gets me so fucking hard. I put my hand through your hair as you unbuckle my pants. Karen joins and kisses your lips, then looks and kisses mine. You undo my pants and stroke my cock, then looking at Karen. She starts sucking as I kiss your lips and take your hoodie off. I fucking love your body. You're a weapon of joy. Karen spits on my cock and strokes, then stands up and kisses you again. You're the best kisser, like my Uncle Tony. You lay on the bed as Karen pulls your purple thong off. Bye bye Miss Piggy. Are pigs purple or pink or both? I'll ask you later. You look at me and reach for my cock as Karen lips kiss your thighs. Slowly licking your wet lips and sliding her tongue inside as you close your eyes and moan, hand on my cock, breathing heavy, starting to stroke. You breathe deeper and deeper, getting wetter and wetter. Karen sucking on your clit as I get on the bed next to you. You're so fucking turned on, I love it. Dripping wet. Spitting on my cock. Sucking it as I start to fuck your head. Karen fucking your soaking pussy with her tongue. You start to cum in her mouth and suck even harder. You take my cock out as Karen climbs on top of you, licking your lips with her juice covered tongue. She climbs fully on top as you get lost kissing her softly. I stand behind you both off the bed. Rubbing your pussies. You're soaking. Her dripping onto yours. Two wet piggies out at the market. You move back on the bed as you kiss, rubbing her nipples as I pinch softly on yours. You reach for my hard cock and slide it inside. First your soaking pussy, then hers. I put my hand on her back, pressing her tighter on you. Pulling your hair as I start fucking you deeper and deeper. Pussy drenched, soaked on my cock. Rubbing Karen's clit as she starts to cum on you. Watching you kiss her as I fuck you deeper and deeper. "You're a good girl," I tell you, looking at me and moaning. Karen kissing your neck as I grab your hair. Our bodies on you. Your beautiful fucking eyes looking at me. "Cum for me," you tell me. Good girl. I squeeze your neck as I shoot inside. "Cum in her," you tell me. Fuck. I pull out and start fucking Karen. She lets out an orgasmic wave as I fuck her deep on top of you. I shoot inside and kiss your lips. Fuck me pink. You're a hot fucking frog. Feels like I'm back in the barn again. I pull out and shoot on Karen's back. You open your mouth as some hits your face. Three of us pause. Panting. Hot. Heavy. Sweating. Fucked. Cum. Malibu. Burning. Poor Bernie. The army. It's sad. So fucking sad. But fuck me, you're a hot little piggy. You frog fucker.

MUCKY CUNT

It's Sunday. The Lord's Day. The holiest of them all. Malibu is burning. Bernie dropped out. The virus is still spreading.

It's sad. So sad. But at least Mass is on. The virus can't find us in there. Jesus has our back. We've been locked up inside for three weeks. You've been a good cunt to quarantine with. Doing laundry like a good dungeon girl. I like it. You come to Mass with me pretending you're holy. We're going to workout after. It's a bad idea. You fuck. You look too hot. A real prick. In your black and red yoga pants. Your black and white yoga top. Walking to church, looking at you pissed off and turned on. Reminds me of how Father Brendan would look at me while I sang in the choir back in school. In my tight grey pants and mucky wellies. He loved those pants. He would tell me all the time. We get to Mass as they're singing the opening hymn. Ava Maria. My favourite. You smile and try to kiss my cheek. I push you away. "Social distancing," I tell you. Not now devil fucker, not in Jesus's house. You look upset and pout. I like it. You deserve it. But fuck your ass looks too hot in those devil pants. Sister Mary O'Rourke warned us about women like you growing up. Pure heathens. The Mary Magdalenes of the world. I want to pin you down and spit on your face. Help you repent so you make it to heaven. Through the pearly gates with your dirty devil soul. You look beautiful you hot fuck, like a cup of tea on a rainy Irish day. You start to sing Ava Maria. It's some of the worst singing I've ever heard. You're oblivious. Like a drunk frog warbling muck. You look at me and smile. Bastard. Now I like you again. "I like Mass," you whisper at me, "It gets me so turned on." How dare you. Jesus can hear us. Your nipples are hard. It's turning me on. I want you naked. You look down see that I'm hard. "This is your fucking fault," I tell you. "I'm sorry, Father. Forgive me." you reply. Oh you're a fuck. A bootsy cunt. "You're in trouble," I whisper in your ear. "I'm sorry," no reply, genuinely. It's too late. I take your hard and lead you down the pew. Pew pew. Touching you gets us both even harnier. I'm sorry Jesus. I'll teach her the truth. "You have to stop," I tell you, outside in the foyer. "Stop what?" you ask. "Oh shut the fuck up." I lead you to the bathroom and lock the door. This is how it's going to be. You cucky munt. Reminds me of when my school principal, Mr. O'Toole, would bend me over his lap and punish me in his office. I was 18. Harny boy. You're a harny girl. I kiss your lips as I squeeze your neck. "You're turning me on too much," I tell you. You look at me with sad dad eyes. I squeeze your neck tighter and spit in your mouth. You smile and close your eyes. I turn you around against the sink and pull your pants down. Slapping your ass hard as I choke you. Looking at you in the mirror. You hot fucker. You wince as I spank again. Ass red. Moaning loud. You're too loud. I grab the bathroom bible and gag your mouth. Slap you hard again as you gag and moan into the Bible. That's better. Your pussy is soaking, like a wet bog June. You hot bog woman. I spank again as your stomach breathes deeper. The choir is singing. The birds are watching. God is here. You're being punished. "Touch your clit," I tell you. You do as you're told. Clit swollen and throbbing. I press your hand harder on it. Sliding my rock hard cock inside your dripping pleasure pond pussy. You bite hard on the Bible as Jesus takes the wheel and fucks you deep. Your pussy drenched on my cock. Like a sock that stood in a puddle. You're a mess. A wet cunt of a mess. I spank you hard and grab your hair. Silently fucking you for the Lord. Spitting on your back and looking at you in the mirror. You're a hot fuck. I pull your hair and rub your clit as your legs shake. Cumming on my cock as you bite the Bible. The first wave making you gush hard. Sinning on me. Becoming a good girl. The bathroom door twists but I have it locked. I tell you to shush as I keep slowly fucking you. Deeper and deeper. Choking your neck while I watch you. We're missing Mass. Father Brendan would be so upset. The shame hits me as I'm deep in you. It's too harny. I'm going to cum. I pull out and tell you to get on your knees. You do as you're told. Bible in your mouth. Eyes open. You're a good girl. I cum on your face and lips. Fuck you. You hot fuck. Cumming on the Bible by mistake. Oh dear Jesus. You smile with your eyes up at me. "Lick it off," I tell you. You lick the Bible and swallow my cum, like a thirsty Jesus returning from a 40-day stroll in the desert. Your drought quenched. Your throat blessed. Your ass red raw. Malibu is burning. Bernie is out. We're missing Mass. It's sad. So sad. But you're a hot cunt. And Jesus forgives. You beautiful mucky bootsy bastard.

PINEAPPLE PUSSY

It's Thursday. International Horny Day. Every day is harny day.
It's quarantine. We're all broken and harny. Malibu is burning.
Biden sniffed some hair. Trump can't pronounce words. You're
too broken to cum. It's sad. So sad. But at least you can cum on
your own. You sent me a video of you squirting. On your knees
in your bedroom. Like you're praying to God. Reaching out to
Jesus. Touching Mother Mary. Like Father Brennan reaching
out and touching me. Fiddling. Fondling. Filling with me the
Holy Spirit. Our Father. Who art. Who whom. Who whomst.
You started pressing your vibrator on your clit and squirting. It
was so hot. The video got me so harny. My mind went dancing.
Dancing for days. I'm meant to be at mine working but you filled
up my mind. A light down a well. A torch in the night. A ferry
in little car. A scream in the alley. Oh the harn. A book arrived
for you at mine. The Tao of Pooh. To help your mind. Cure the
dancer. I want to touch and fuck and taste you. Like the holiest
communion. I can't write. Too harny. It's the day. Fuck it. I'm
coming over. I text. "I have your book." You reply. "Come bring
it to me. Let's stroll." Let's stroll indeed. I park by yours and
you come out. Your dog Bozo bounding alongside. He's a feisty
fucker. Bouncing around. His balls still intact. Lucky bastard.
You look fucking hot. Your white top and green pants. Your hot
stomach and beanie hat. Your mask making your eyes dance
out. Those darting bastards, like two drunk swallows in the sky.
I want to fuck you right now on the street. But it's bright. The
golden hour. And society. At least we have our masks. I spot a
couple of goons without them on. Faces condomless. So sad. So
mad. Makes me harny. We stroll. Benny Bozo is leaping. You're
talking. You've been selling feet photos all day. I've been writing
sextpoems. We've been in the sex trade since quarantine. Sex
sells. Buy me. I'm getting too turned on thinking about you on
your knees squirting. "What kind of dog is Benny Bozo?" I ask.
I know. But my brain is dumb. "A Meranian," you tell me. "It's

like the cousin of a... oh I forgot the name. What's the dog in the movies, kind of evil one?" I don't know. "I don't know," I repeat out loud. I like looking at your stomach. And your lower back. I want my hands around them. Pinning you down. We walk past a couple, both wearing masks. Good maskies. "Did you like my video?" you ask. "I fucking loved it." It replays in my mind and I'm hard again. For fuck's sake. You see me adjusting my ponder pipe. "That's hot," you say with a twinkle in your eye, "I want to taste." I smile and my ponder pipes harder. Your eyes. They're the best. Two global dancers. We walk past the 101 freeway. Two homeless people are having sex in a tent. Daytime outdoor sober sex. Maybe they're drunk. Who knows. It's a cool tent. Reminds me of when my Uncle Joe took me camping. Joey Pizza I would call him. He'd feed me pizza in the dark of the night and make sure I knew how to take off and put on my belt. He'd always be doing it to me. Great pizza. Extra pineapple. Fuck. I want your lips. "Come," you tell me, cutting off the main street. I follow your lead, Benny Bozo alongside. Down an alley behind some dumpsters. My favourite. "I don't think I'm broken any more," you tell me, pulling down your mask. I tie Benny to a pole and look around. Just us. I kiss your beautiful lips like a sailor on a dock. Who's the whure, not too sure. Your lips are wet and body warm. Hands on your waist. Pulling you into me. My hard cock pressed against you. Your hard nipples pushing through your top, trying to break free, like Nelson Mandela, that time he was in jail. I slide my hand down your workout pants and feel your soaking pussy. Sweet Jesus. You're back. You're not broken. You're drenched on my hand, lips kissing, your hand on my cock, stroking as I rub your clit. You pull your pants down for me as I do the same. You look me in the eye as you rub your clit. Staring at me, breathing deeper, heavier, like a mountain dew. I'm stroking my cock watching you, pulling on your hard nipples, eyes locked on yours. You're rubbing your clit back and forth, biting your lip, my fingers inside, my cock covered in precum. "Cum for me," I tell you, watching you go deeper and deeper. You rub faster and faster and stomach clenches as you cum fucking hard. Pigeons scatter into the air as you let out a moan of joy, your sweet pineapple pussy exploding like a diamond in the sky. Squirting on me as you cum hard. Grabbing my arm and cumming on my cock, your mouth open and barely able to breathe. Oh you hot fucker. You agape beauty. You're rubbing your pussy juice on my cock and grabbing me to kiss. You've broken free. You're back. Mercury is over. I've no clue. You're sliding my cock inside you as I wrap your legs around me. Fucking you deep against the alley wall. Your wet pussy sliding up and down my cock, like firemen slipping down the pole. I'm kissing you hard as I get harder and harder inside your tight sloppy pussy. Like a drunk at 3AM, sloppy and messy. Squeezing your neck as I cum inside you. Shooting deep like a turnip in the sea. Kissing you hard as I cum again. Your cum dripping down my cock. You rubbing your clit as I keep fucking you. The sun setting. The golden hour. Your golden shower. All over my cock-a-whom. You start to cum again, your eyes lighting up. "Doberman!" you yell, riding my cock like a saddle ranch bull. Oh yeah. That's the evil dog. A homeless man pops his head out of the dumpster "Dad?" You scuttle off me and pull your pants up. I pull mine and we scuttle off down the alley. Benny Bozo running alongside. Balls flapping in the wind. I'm still hard. You're still harny. You hot fuck. It's a harny day. Malibu. Burning. Biden. Touching. Trump. Trumping. It's sad. So sad. Was that my son. Who knows. But you're a good girl.

CAKE FUCKER

It's Sunday. The day of our Lord. Michael Jordan. His doc is on ESPN later. Can't wait. And Mass? What a day. And it's your birthday. I almost forgot. You got upset. Malibu is burning. The mailman might have stolen your birthday present. Florida is opening its beaches again. It's sad. So sad. But at least I bought you birthday cake. Make up for the missing present. Tom Ford shoes. You would've looked so hot in them. Ah well. Alas. Next year. Please God. Who knows. We walked by Bristol Farms on our way to church. You had been reading all morn. The Diary of Anne Frank. You felt bad for her but also could relate. Because we are locked up now too. You told me this while drinking a white claw. Said this was like our World War II. Then we walked to church. You're so right. I must read the book next. Find out if she would've been a Belieber or not. We got you some chocolate cake and a carrot and a banana. You're a hungry girl. You deserve the best. I bought you the finest carrot. Father Joe Finnerty is giving a lovely sermon. About Jesus or Buddha. I can't fully tell. You're eating a banana and turning me on. Every time you eat a banana I get hard. Maybe it's a mental illness of mine. But it reminds me of my old cow Jenny. You have the same eyes as her. Both of you would stare at me while eating a banana. Big beautiful cow eyes. I'm hard as fuck at Mass. Sorry, Jesus. Sorry, Father Joe. "I'm hella wet," you whisper in my ear. You just started using that word lately. Hella. Maybe it's from the diary you're reading. Anne hella Frank. I presume so. "I'm hella harny," I whisper back. You're still eating the banana. Looking at me. The smell of mango white claw off your breath. I want to fuck you stupid. "Come," I tell you, leading you down the pew. Squeezing past the old couple who had been eying us up. Sally and Bernie, the local cuck couple. Bernie is always trying to get me to fuck his wife. They're in their 80s. She's a sweet woman. Tender lover. Bernie is more rugged. Like a cold piece of oak on a hot spring break underneath the winter breeze and salmon summer fall. So true, I think to myself, so true. We get outside and I spin you around. Your beautiful cow eyes looking at me. Jesus. What are you wearing to mass. A black zip up hoodie and peach shorts. You peach fucker. A white van drives by. Reminds me of the one that used to kidnap me when I was young. Those were the days. I would eat so many sweets. This white van has black trash bags on the roof. Piles and piles of trash. Kind of reminds me of you. The tone. I kiss your white claw mouth and pull you close. "I'm so wet for you Father," you tell me. You're a good girl. I slide my hand down your shorts. You're soaking. Drenched. Your peach thong like a wet sock of hope. You beautiful cow. I lead you down the garden path into the church gardens. It's wild here. Flowers and birds and bear in the distance, some big hairy gay dude walking his little dog. I pin you against the church wall and feel your wet pussy. It's like a cow's tongue dripping with milk. I love pinning you down. I want you naked. I slide your shorts down and push your thong to the side. You unzip your hoodie. Nothing underneath. You beautiful fuck cunt. Squeezing your neck and kissing your World War II lips. Thinking about poor Anne. "Fuck me sis," you whisper into my ear. That's your new thing too. Calling me sis. It's very odd. And gets me hard. I want your birthday lips on my cock first. I open your birthday cake box and feed you some. Smear it on your lips. You grab a handful and eat half, then stroke my cock with the rest. Red velvet birthday cock. Rubbing your swollen clit as you stroke my hard velvet. Sliding two fingers inside as you moan louder. Deeper and wetter. Dripping on my hand. Putting cake in your mouth to muffle the moans, like a man with a van stuffing my mouth with his sock. Fun times. "I'm finna cum Daddy," you moan louder, cumming on my hand as I squeeze your neck tighter. You gonna finna cum so hard. I love it. Finna best. Your Brown Betty cow eyes stare me down as you stroke my cake cock. You get on your knees and start sucking like a good girl. Licking the cake off like it's a bowl of icing. Looking up at me with your beautiful eyes. You're the most beautiful fucker. A complete fucker. You'll be the death of me. I pull you to your feet, face against the wall. Grab some more cake and rub it on my hard cock. Sliding inside your soaking tight pussy. You cake fucker. Slapping your ass hard as you ride back on my cock. Grabbing your hard nipples and tits. Pulling your nipples as I go deep inside, like a lost child down a cave. I spank you harder and grab your hair. You rubbing your clit and moaning like a good girl. Cake filling you up like the body of Christ. I grab a handful and rub it off your clit. The velvet mix makes you even wetter. You cum hard on my cock as I spank your ass red velvet raw. You sexy fucker. Your tight pussy squeezing on my cock. Fuck your wet pussy feels amazing. I turn you around and you get on your knees. Face covered in cake. I cum hard on your tits and face. Covering your mouth and lips. You smile and lick. I cum again and hit your eye by mistake. Oh no, your cow eye. It shuts tight but you keep licking, like a pirate in love with an ice cream. You rub my cum and cake off your tits and smile. Your one good eye looking at me in delight. Malibu is burning. The Tom Fords are gone. Florida is Florida. It's sad. So sad. But it's your birthday. You beautiful fuck. A true cake fucker. Happy birthday creep.

HOT OTTER

It's Friday. May 1st. Day one. The first of May. Malibu is burning. Biden is in trouble. The virus is winning and lingering. Loitering like an unwelcome one night stand. It's sad. So sad. But at least we got to pay rent today, so that's nice. A nice little treat. You bought some new lingerie too. Black stuff. I never know what it's called. Looks like leather bondage straps. It's fucking hot. A thong with two straps wrapped around your waist. Riding high up your ass. Black strap bra. "It's a pity I'm bad with words or I would describe it better," I said to you when I first saw it on. You nodded and laughed. You're wearing it now, underneath your oversized black tee. Your black Nike Jordan's. You're a hot fucker. We're doing errands. Getting coffee. There's a line at Coffee Bean. A homeless guy is asking me if I would like to see his tree. Maybe he's not homeless. He's wearing Gucci. Just a rich nut. I decline and turn to you. "What are you watching?" I ask. You look up from your phone "Stepdad porn." Oh. Nice. As you do. Lining up for coffee. Sexy fucker. We order and go wait outside. Hanging in the car park. It's hot. The guy is pointing out his tree. I'm sitting on a wall. You're looking fucking savage. "Come here," I tell you. You do as you're told, like a good girl. Sliding in between my legs. "I'm so horny," you whisper in my ear. "I know, I'm harny too." I tell you, sliding my hand under your t-shirt. Running my fingers down your back, looking at you as I undo your bra. Feeling it come loose as your tits are set free, like two happy Nelson Mandelas. I rub and pull your nipples, feeling them get harder as I lightly pinch and squeeze. Feeling your breath deepen as I pull on them. "Not here," you tell me.

"Shh. I'm going to make you cum." You close your eyes as I move one hand up your body to squeeze your neck, feeling your stomach and pulling your straps with the other. Sliding your thong down so it's loose. Watching your face as I rub your clit. It's already swollen. You love stepdad porn. Bad girl. Your clit is throbbing. Like a sea otter in the cold crystal night. Bobbing away. My finger rubbing slowly over and back. Feeling you get more and more turned on. Wetter and wetter. You're a good girl. "You like that?" I ask you, feeling how soaked your pussy is now. "Yes Daddy," you tell me. Submissive and mine. Squeezing your neck as the old man talks to the tree nearby. "I'm so wet Daddy", you tell me again, like it's a bad thing. "I know. You're a good girl," I tell you, feeling your ass and grabbing hard. I'm going to fuck that after. Your hips started moving into me as your clit gets bigger and bigger, your pussy wetter and wetter. Reminds me of the time I got caught in the rain coming home from church that one time. Father Timmy saw me and took me to his place to dry me off. Stripped me down and had me take a hot shower. He even got in and helped by washing me down. A kind man. A gentle touch. A tender touch. Like my finger, inside your tight wet pussy. Two sliding in, beckoning you, pulling you into me, like the tide with a wave. Dripping on my hand as I press on your clit. Squeezing your neck as I feel you breathing harder. Pulling you close as you start to moan louder. People driving by. Men shouting at trees. Cars. Women. Just shouting. You moaning. "Not here," you say, close to cumming. You're reluctant. "Cum for me," I tell you, "Like a good girl." You do as you're told and let loose, lost in the moment and moaning loud. Cumming as I finger you, pressing on your clit. Squeezing your neck. I love making you cum in public. You're so polite. No one would know you're my hot slut. You kiss me hard as you cum, slowly stopping and breathing hard. "Fuck me Daddy," you whisper in my ear. You're a hot fucker. I like when you're aggressive. "Come." I lead you to the bathroom inside the Coffee Bean, like Father Timmy walking me into the shower stall. Our masks are on. We're inside. I like it. We're fucking with them on. You stroke my cock as I look in your sea driven eyes. You really are a hot seal. A land otter. A human fish. I don't know, I'm harny as fuck. And you're stroking me so good. You lift your mask up and spit on my cock, kneeling down to taste it. Licking my precum. You love tasting it. Like a cup of tea on a May morn. You spit on it again, then turn around and bend over the sink. You spit on your hand and wait for me to pull your thong down. "Fuck my ass, Daddy." you tell me. Good fucking girl. You rub your spit on your tight hole as I slide my hard cock slowly inside. Filling you up like the donut that you are. A real Krispy Kreme. You moan loud as my cock slides deeper and deeper. "Cover your mouth," I tell you. Mask on. Cock inside. Slowly fucking. Eyes lighting up. Joy and terror. Your tight ass. My big cock. Hard and deep. Pounding you. Deeper and deeper. Fucking you hard against the sink. Spanking your ass hard and pulling your hair. You're my good girl. Hot slut. Fucking and spanking. Riding back on my cock. Rubbing your clit as I fuck you deeper. Looking at your eyes all dancing. You love it. I love it. Two dirty whores. Like Father Timmy and Bishop Brendan. They taught me well. Squeezing your neck as I pound you hard. Your tight ass filling up and clenching on my cock. Feeling your clit swell and pussy gush. Your hand on the mirror. Spanking your ass as you start to cum again, pressing on your clit. Spanking you red raw as I start to cum with you. Filling you up. Shooting deep inside. You're fucking beautiful. Looking at you in the mirror. I love watching you. You good girl. Hanging on the sink, fucked and my cum inside you. Slowly pulling out. Watching as my cum drips out of your ass and down your thighs. You take a finger and wipe it up, then swallow it. You're a hot otter. Dirty whore. Malibu is burning. Biden. Virus. Rent. It's sad. So sad. But fuck me. I love coffee. Big mood.

CHATEAU

It's Thursday. I think. I don't know. It's all a blur. My AC is broken. Malibu is burning. The hornets are coming. It's sad.

So sad. I've been squatting in an empty apartment. Sleeping on the floor. Eating burgers drunk off the carpet. It's been fun. But sad. So sad. Me hips are killing me. So I checked into a hotel for the night. Chateau Marmont. The only one open. The only one with the pool. The only one you'd come visit at. You've been in self quarantine. It's been 10 days since we fucked. 10 days in the worst heat. 10 days of battering our genitals over Skype and Zoom. I did a group chat on FaceTime. It wasn't pretty. Too many people saw my white thighs. Eyes lit up. They're stunning thighs. Porcelain, like a vase. One of those things you put flowers in. Or drink out of if you're drunk. My Uncle Greg would fill the vase full of his Jesus juice and I would drink it down. Tasted like asparagus. But that's neither here nor there or quare. We're in heat. Like Al Pacino and Robert De Niro. Two harny lads. I've never been so cooped up. Like a randy rooster. I've been reading Anne Frank's Diary. Similar paths. Similar plights. I'm only on page one so I'm not sure what happens but I can tell we're two icons. I'm trying to read by the pool. You're laying next to me. Looking too fucking hot. Like a 99 ice cream on a mild day in Ireland. Dripping wet. All over the place. I want to lick the sweat off you. Your body is a weapon. My body is a waterfall. I'm roasting. And hard as fuck for you, like an applied maths question in a summer exam. My brain is frying. Watching the sweat roll down your neck. Between your beautiful tits. In your cream bikini. I want to rip it off. Beads of sweat on your hot stomach. Your legs and waist frying in the sun. Sweat dripping. Your pretty pussy covered in a cream bikini bottom thong. I want to undo the strings and taste between your legs. Your pineapple pussy dripping on my chin. You're a juicy fucker. Lying in the sun at the chateau. You open your eyes and reach for me. Hand on my cock. I'm rock hard. Bursting through my stunning yellow shorts. Like a sunflower about to bloom. Like Father Bloom about to burst open into song, all over my face. I miss the choir. The joy of it all. The high notes and the low blows. I want your lips on my cock. "I'm ready to ride that cock," you tell me, shading your eyes from the sun. There's no one around. I don't know. Maybe there is. I'm harny and I've blinkers on. You're rubbing my cock through my shorts. Your nipples are getting hard. I want your pussy exploding on me. I take you by the hand and lead you to the outdoor shower. Close the wooden door. I don't care who sees. I turn on the shower and kiss you under the sun and rain. Jesus you're beautiful. Like a cup of tea that's freshly made by my Aunt June. Lovely woman, bad fake teeth. They'd always pop out kissing me. You have my cock out of my shorts and are on your knees. Sucking for dear life. Water pouring down on us. Eyes closed. Water over my ears. I could be anywhere. In the jungle. Being sucked off by a parrot and a snake. Jesus I'm too harny. I open my eyes and look at you sucking my balls. Rubbing my cock between your beautiful wet tits. Slapping your mouth. I squeeze your neck. You smile and suck again. Like a good girl. Spreading your legs and undoing your bikini strings. Thong falling off. Rubbing your clit. My hand on your hair. Holding your head as you suck. And rub. And touch. Fucking your mouth. I feel you getting more turned on. Rubbing your clit. Soaked under water. Looking at me as you pull back. Water pouring down your body. Rubbing your clit. Standing up and spreading your legs, hands on the wall. I slide my cock inside your tight wet pussy from behind. Grabbing your ass and spanking. Splatters of water like a piece of art. You Picasso fucker. Dripping on my cock. Your clit throbbing. Your pussy squeezing. Pulling your hair. Filling you deep. Pressing you against the wall. Fucking you hard. You're a good girl. "Harder Daddy," you whisper. You're a good little slut. I spank you harder and fuck you deeper again. I feel you reaching and grabbing. Pulling me in. Holding the wall. Cumming on my cock as I fuck you hard. Covering your mouth as you moan and cum for Ireland. 10 days of pent up glory. All over my cock. Fucking back on it again as you cum more. You're a good girl. I want to dominate the fuck out of you. I squeeze your neck and grab your back as I cum inside you. Shooting hard. Like broken stars. Clattering. I'm gone. You feel amazing. Cumming inside you again. Feel your ass and pussy squeezing on me. You sexy fuck. I love that ass. "Keep the cum inside you," I tell you, tying up your thong and wrapping a towel around you. I do the same. Shorts and bra are left behind. I lead you through the pool side to our bungalow. Nod hello at the old man Trevor, the pool attendant. He saw it all but he's as gay as Christmas. He winks and says nothing. A lovely wink. A lovely winker. You open the bungalow door and walk inside. Dropping the towel as you climb onto the bed. Looking at yourself in the wardrobe mirror. You beautiful fuck. Your body is the best I've seen. Watching me look at your pussy and ass. My cum dripping down your pussy and legs. You're a good girl. You kept it in. I kiss your ass and spank a cheek. You bite a lip and smile in the mirror. I spank again as you moan. Rubbing your tight asshole with coconut oil and lathering up my cock. Slowly sliding inside your sexy beautiful ass. Slowly. Easy. Filling you up. Your mouth open. Afraid to moan. Until you know you're good. I am in. Like Flynn. Fucking you slowly in the ass. Watching you in the mirror. You're a beautiful dancer. Back and forth as my cock goes deeper. Rubbing your clit as you look at me, mouth open. "Cum for me," I tell you. You rub harder as my cock goes deeper. Your golden brown ass. Squeezing as you cum again. Holding you down by your lower back. Watching you in the mirror. Malibu is burning. Poor Anne. My AC. The hornets. It's sad. So sad. But fuck me, you're a good girl. I'm going to cum in your tight fucking ass.

HONEY GOD

It's Thursday. I think. Who knows. The days and nights are all the same. Long and dull and harny. Malibu is burning. Biden is running. The virus is winning. It's sad. So sad. But I went to get us coffee. You stayed at home to do laundry. Like a good girl. I just want to fuck you all day when you're doing laundry. All lazy and hot and trying on new clothes. When I left you were wearing a waist trainer and black Calvin's and brown boots. It was a look. I walk back in with coffee and you're in a grey bodysuit and denim shorts. The smallest shorts. You hot fucker. On your toes reading something on your phone. "I might start making honey," you tell me, not looking up. "Oh yeah?" "Yeah. We must save the bees." So true. No clue what you're on about. You queen bee. Hot honey god. "People are getting chin jobs too for the summer," you say, taking your coffee. "Oh yeah." I say again, lost. "Should I?" you ask. "No you fuck, you have the hottest chin. Shh," I reply. You smile and look at me. "You like it?" "I do." You like my balls on your chin, that's why I love it. "Are you thinking of your sad, weary balls on my chin?" you ask. "They're not sad, they're happy weary balls." I pin you against the kitchen counter and kiss your lips. They're like onion buds blooming. I love your lips. Reminds me of Father Tommy back in Ireland growing up, lovely lips on him, as every aunt would say. He loved to kiss us all on the cheeks. Frisky Father Tommy. A gentle man. I unbutton your shorts and kiss you hard. Tug them down your waist as they slide down your long neon legs to the floor. You taste like tequila. And your hair's wet. The hottest. Slicked back. Like a female American Psycho. I pull your bodysuit down your shoulder, admiring your beautiful boobs. Hard nipples taunting me. I kiss your neck and pinch them, getting them harder and harder. Pulling your body suit down your legs. You naked honey god. Standing in the kitchen. All mine. You hot fucking bee. I turn you around and bend you over the kitchen counter. "Spread your legs," I tell you. You do as you're told. Grabbing your hair and neck as you feel me hard against your ass through my jeans. Spitting on your back and kissing it as I feel your lower back and ass. Kissing your cheeks as I press your tight honey ass with my finger. Seeing your wet pussy breathing for me. Dying for me to slide inside. Your honey pot. You are Winnie the Pooh. You hot fuck. I taste your pussy lips and lick your tight ass. You moan and spread your legs more. Standing on your toes. Dying for me inside you. Not yet. You must be a good girl first. I take your hands behind your back and lead you to the bedroom. A cop and the dirty whore. Leading you from behind. Hand on your neck. Laundry on the bed. I push you down and flip you over. Naked and facing me. Tying your hands to the bedpost, feet to the bottom. You're spread like a star for me. I watch you as I strip naked. Kissing your legs and thighs as I make my way onto you.

Looking in the double wardrobe mirror at you as I'm kneeling over you. Fingering your wet pussy and pinching your nipples. Both of us looking in the mirror. Watching me get harder and harder as you get wetter and wetter, like a sad funeral on a summer's day. Two fingers inside as you're spread like an X. Touching your g-spot as you moan deeper and deeper. Pinching your nipples hard. You're helpless and soaked. I'm hard and on top of you. Watching you. Your beautiful body in the mirror. Moaning and tongue yearning. Wanting to taste my cock. "Open your mouth," I tell you. You open and I grab your face. Slap it and spit in your mouth. You moan and close your eyes as my fingers go deeper. Palm pressing on your clit. Finger pressing on your tight ass. You are the honey god. You sexy fuck. I kneel over you and rest my happy balls on your chin. You smile and run your tongue on my rock hard cock. Up and down like a ice cream cone. Licking and trying to get it in your mouth. I slap my cock off your face and spit in your mouth again. You reach for my cock and start sucking. Wet hair. Wet pussy. Wet balls. I'm pulling your nipples as you suck and lick, moaning and getting wetter. Balls in your mouth as I stroke myself. "Look in the mirror," I tell you, your feet and hands clenching as your pussy gets wetter and wetter. You look as I squeeze your neck. My cock resting on your cheek. Your honey pot ready to burst. I want to taste. I slap your face and kiss your nipples. Sucking hard. Watching you squirm, like a good girl. Like me trying to get away from Father Tommy's wet lips. He loved to French kiss after mass, the horny whure. I taste your clit as I finger your pussy. Pressing on your tight ass, then kissing it. Hearing you moan louder as my tongue slides inside. Squirming and writhing on the white linen sheets. You washed them. Good girl. I'm so fucking hard for you. I kneel over you again and start fucking your mouth. Grabbing the back of your head as I fuck you hard. Hand on your clit and hand on your head. You're my good girl. My cock comes out drenched in your spit. I rub it on your face then pin you down by the neck. My hard cock sliding deep inside your soaking pussy. You dripping honey on me. Filling you up as your eyes look at me in pleasure and pain. I squeeze harder as I start fucking you slow. Your legs spread and arms tied. Wet pussy dripping on the sheets. Watching you as I fuck you hard. Soaked hard cock and squeezing your sexy neck. Pulling your nipples and grabbing your tits as I fuck you deeper. Slowly. Riding. Fucking. Dripping. "Open your mouth." You do as you're told as I spit again. I slide out of you and kneel over you again. Watching you in the mirror as I hold your head and fuck your mouth. Fingering your pussy as your face is fucked. Feeling your legs clench and tighten and body burst as you cum for me. Sucking harder as you cum. Moaning into my cock, like a kidnapped child. I press on your clit with my palm as I keep fingering you. Playing with your tight ass. I untie you're hands as you suck. Pull out and slap your beautiful face. Untying your feet. "Get on top," I tell you. You do as you're told. Hot and wet and horny. I lie down as you climb on top. My cock sliding inside your soaking pussy. Fuck you feel so good. "You like that, you honey fuck?" I ask. "Yes Daddy," you tell me. Riding my cock. I'm kissing your tits and sucking your nipples. You're riding hard and moaning loud. You're lost. You're good. You're Winnie the fucking Pooh. Cumming again on me as you fuck my hard cock. Screaming. Biting your nipple as I watch us in the mirror. Cumming with you. Shooting deep. Looking at you in the eye as I cum hard. "Cum for me Daddy." You climb off and start sucking and stroking my cock. Shooting on your face and my body. Smiling and kissing it. Licking my happy weary balls. Watching yourself in the mirror like a fucking honey god as you lick and swallow my cum. Malibu is burning. Biden is running. The sheets are ruined. It's sad. So sad. But fuck me pink, you're a good girl.

EMERALD ISLE

It's Tuesday. The day of Mother Mary. A lovely woman. A virgin. Like myself. So tender. So loving. So harny. It's too hot out. Malibu is burning. The Atlantic is laying people off. It's sad. So sad. I was at coffee with two buddies. Trying to think my mind off it all. But we got kicked out of the car park. Loitering. Like we were 12. True bad boys. So now I'm home. With your iced Americano. And a scone. You love a good scone. I left and you were doing the dishes. In your pyjamas. Like a good quarantine girl. I walk in and you're in the bedroom. "I have your coffee, fucker!" I yell out, like how my uncle Francis used to yell out to me. "Come milk the cows!" he'd say, then I'd run off to meet him in the dark barn. Never saw the cows. You walk out of the bedroom. The click of the heels on the hardwood floor. Reminds me of Father Gerry walking up to the altar. Click. Click. Click. The sounds still turns me on. Jesus fucking Christ. You look fucking unreal. "What the fuck?" I ask like a fool. You're in your new tight dark green dress, black tights, and black heels, hair in half a ponytail, the rest flowing down your shoulders. You look fucking amazing. Your emerald earrings and emerald ring. We're locked inside but you still love to dress up. You're a good girl. I'm too hot, too frustrated, too harny. I'm going to fuck you stupid, like a science exam I actually studied for. "Do you like my new dress?" you ask. I'm turned on and hard just looking at you. I walk over and put your drink on the counter. You're my height almost in your heels. You hot fuck. You take a sip of the coffee, your beautiful lips squeezing on the straw, like a young calf sucking on a tit. Your beautiful cow eyes looking at me. I push your hair behind your ears to look at your emeralds. Reminds me of home. My Aunt Bernice had the same style earrings, same beautiful body too. You hot Bernice. You stand closer to me, I can feel your breath on me. Feels like Father Gerry as he served me holy communion, he loved approaching me from the rear and slipping it into my mouth. "I like your dress," I tell you, "Now take it off." You turn around and lift up your hair. I undo the zipper and zip it open. You slide it down your shoulders and body, until it rests on your waist. I touch your back and kiss your neck from behind. "Take it off," I tell you. You slide it down your waist and legs to the floor, then step out of it. Wearing just your heels, tights and jewellery. You're a beautiful cunt. I love it. You turn around looking scared. Your body looks so glorious. Nipples hard. Stomach tight. Pussy shaved. You're a dream. Father

Gerry used to tell me the same as he eyed me up and down. A tender man, with a tender touch. Like a skilled spoons player, he taught me how to fiddle. I kiss your lips and pull you close. Your nails on my back as I kiss your neck and lips, biting your beautiful floppy lower one. I push you against the doorway as we kiss hard. My hand in your hair, holding your head, squeezing your neck, moving you to the bedroom, pulling and pinching your hard nipples. "Get on your knees," I tell you. You do as you're told. Mouth open. Waiting for my cock. Like me when I was young, waiting for Uncle Francis to squeeze some milk into my mouth. It was a dark barn. I strip naked while watching you. You're a classy fucker. The most beautiful. With the most deviant mind. You feel bossy in your tights and heels. I know it. You take my cock in your mouth and start sucking. Feeling it get harder and harder, like that block of cheese in the back of the fridge. Gagging as you deepthroat, gasping for air as you take it all the way out. Spit dripping down your chin. Lips soaked like a McDonalds bathroom floor. You lick my cock up and down and swallow it full again. Your earrings catching the light. You're the Emerald Isle now. You hot fuck. I want you sweating. You gag on my cock again and pull it out. Precum and spit dripping off it. Your chin soaked. I stand you up and push you on the bed. Kiss your wet lips as I get on top of you. My hard wet cock between your legs. Your heels wrapped around me. Pushing me closer to your pleasure pond. Your golden pussy. Dripping and tight. Soaked and begging. Dying for me inside you. You tilt your head and open your mouth. I spit inside then squeeze your neck. My cock sliding inside your dream pool pussy, like Tom Cruise on a marble floor. I'm choking you as I slowly fuck you, watching as your eyes close and face smiles, neck and back arching. Pulling your ass up as I go deeper. Watching you moan and breathe deeper. Wet pussy slapping off my cock. Thighs off your ass. Pinning you down. On the bed. Like a good fucking girl. Slapping your ass. Like a wild horse. You love slapping. You black beauty. A lovey whore horse. Looking at me as I go deeper. Playing with your clit. Pinching your nipples. Breathing quicker. Stomach sucking in. Choking. Squeezing. Harder. Your emerald eyes.

Looking at me. You're close. You hot fuck. You're so fucking wet. Jesus I'm so fucking hard. I pin you down as you start to cum for me. You hot fuck. Your pussy dancing with delight. You lost in the golden light. Like an altar boy stumbling out the back of the church. Father Gerry scrambling behind. The thought makes me harder. Closer to cumming. You look at me and the fire in your eyes. Pushing me back. You get on top. You hot fuck. Choking my neck. Looking at me. Riding my cock. You little horse fucker. Pinning me down as you ride and ride. Grabbing your whip next to the bed. Hitting hard across the body. Pain flashing through me. Getting harder as you whip again. You fuck. I grab you and pull you close. You're going to cum. I feel your pussy gushing on me. Like a sycophant. Our bodies tighten as you cum on me. Good fucking girl. I start cumming with you. Shooting deep inside. Like Jesus down the cave. Like Mary in the stable. Pulling your hair and slapping your face as I cum again. I flip you over and I'm on top. Pulling out and cumming all over your body. Covering you in joy. Your face lighting up as I cum and shoot across your cheeks and lips. Like when the cow and Uncle Francis did with me. It was a dark barn. I never saw the cow. Malibu is burning. The Atlantic. Loitering. It's sad. So sad. But you're a good jockey. You hot Emerald Isle.

SPACE SEX

It's Wednesday. The feast of St. Anthony. A great saint. The patron saint of losing things. I've prayed to him many a time. Earlier this morning. Malibu is burning. The weather ruined the moon. I lost my favourite pair of socks. It's sad. So sad. But hopefully St. Anthony can sort it out. Top man. One of the best. I'm singing a hymn while driving to collect you. My chin is killing me. Hit it off the dining table. Blew up like a balloon. The pain. The anguish. You're at your friend's place. You went to watch the space launch. NASA. SpaceX. One of the two. Maybe both. You're the space nerd. Looking hot leaving earlier. Your

moaning. Touching and rubbing. I love how wet you get giving me head. "Let me feel how wet you are." You lift yourself up to let me feel. Fuck me pink. St. Anthony would be proud. You're drenched and tight as could be, like that crevice between the car seat and the belt buckle. The hard to reach space. Too tight. Feels good. Fucking you is like that. Space sex. You kneel again while I'm rubbing your clit. Sucking and rubbing. "Cum for me," I tell you. You look at me and smile with your eyes. I squeeze your neck while you kiss my cock. Watching you rub your swollen clit. Your soaking pussy. Your belt buckle ass. You start sucking hard as you start to cum. Shaking and sucking. Moaning into my cock, like a stolen pirate. Gagged and slurring. Squirting on the car floor. You hot fuck. I fully recline the seat and you climb on top. Ripping off your t-shirt. Sorry, NASA. Hard nipple in my mouth. Biting hard as you cum again on my cock. Riding like a jockey. Head hitting the roof. Grabbing my hair. Squeezing your neck. Biting your hard nipple and hearing you moan. Pleasure and pain. I cum hard inside you, like a prisoner set free. A man on the run. Wild and loose. Cumming deep inside your glorious galaxy. You keep riding as I stay hard. A horn beeps. A car is blocked. What. The. Fuck. You're off and I'm reversing. We're lost and confused. Floating in space. You're trying to drink Coke. I'm trying to think straight. It's a flash, we get home. A light and back in the apartment. Ripping clothes off. Carrying you to the bed. My head between your legs. Kissing your thighs. Tender, like Father Terry. Licking your pussy and ass, like caretaker Simon, feeding me ice cream. Biting on your clit. My cum dripping out of you. You cumming in my mouth. Holding you down. Pinning you tight. Cumming hard for me. Watching you in the mirror. On your stomach. Looking at each other. Fucking you from behind. Pussy soaking, shaking, tight as fuck. Holding you down. Hands on your lower back. Tight. Taut. Tasty. Hard as fuck inside you. Dominating you from behind. Slapping your sexy ass and pulling your hair. Squeezing your neck as you cum. You're a good girl. I stay inside as I fuck you while cumming. Watching us fuck. Lost in space. Malibu is burning. The weather. The horn. Beeping. It's sad. So sad. But they are my favourite socks. Under the bed. Thanks, St. Anthony. Top man.

POTATO PUSSY

It's Monday. The Pope's day. Lovely fella. Gentle touch. Usually a blessed one but not today. Malibu is burning. Trump is clowning. It's a war zone outside. It's sad. So sad. Protests. BLM. Police starting violence. Looters be looting. It's a mess. There's a curfew. It's still quarantine. It's like being grounded while being grounded. My brain is confused. And I've never been more harny. So turned on. All the fists in the air. The chanting. The burning and dancing. Maybe the weather. Or the nice bowl of porridge I ate earlier. Maybe the porridge. So creamy and soft. Reminded me of Father O' Shea. A creamy, soft porridge himself. How he would feed me in my time of need. The simple life. Back in Ireland. Running through muck. Random boners. Gentle wanks. But the world needs to change. Can't keep killing black people. America is mental. And I'm on a bus. It's the only way to get to your abode. Take four buses. They're stopping cars. Arresting people. You're worth a bus ride though. Like going to a disco in Ireland. Well worth the ride. You've been at the beach all day. I pass a police riot on bus number three. People chanting All Lives Matter. They remind me of my Uncle Tony. He was a cunt. You've been texting me photos of your tanned beach body while I'm bussing. Bus life. I'm hard on a bus. Your ass looks so fucking good. A perfect potato. In your pink bikini. Your perky potato boobs. I want to butter you up. A little butter baby. I must be missing Ireland. Can't stop thinking about potatoes. And fucking you. Like a good girl. Helicopters are everywhere. Police starting shit again. The bus pulls up close to yours. I tuck my hard ponder pipe and stroll to yours. You're in the shower. Texting me photos. Your potato ass all washed and soapy. Looks creamy. You hot potato fucker. Reminds me of my other Uncle Gerry. He loved potatoes. Hated chickens. But loved chicken soup. It was weird. Like too many white Americans. Love black culture. Hate black people. Uncle Gerry was a cunt too. But love a creamy potato. I suppose I do too. The door is open at your apartment. I walk in and strip down. You've left the bathroom door open. I'm hard and naked, like an honest question in the daylight. You see me over your shoulder and turn your ass fully to me. You hot fuck. It's perfect. Like a dream spud. You'd be given castles and cows in Ireland for such a fucking potato ass. I think buses turn me on. Can't shut up about potatoes. I get in the shower. "Hello butter baby." "Hi potato Daddy," you reply. Fuck me pink. Potato Daddy. My favourite. My hard cock pressing against your wet ass. Water running down your perfect body. Your hard nipples and perky tits. Stunning turkey pits. My cock sliding up and down your ass cheeks. Between your legs. Along your tight wet potato pussy. Butter dripping. My hard cock spreading your lips. You're soaking. Your wet body against mine. I turn you around and kiss you against the shower wall. Hand on your neck. Your nails in my back. Choking you slightly. Cock pressed against your stomach. Pulling your hard nipples. Kissing your soft wet lips. Like a seal kissing an otter. Water pouring down. You look fucking beautiful. Like a lake in the moonlight. A true tasty creep. Moaning and mouth opening as my cock slides inside your tight wet pussy. Choking you tighter as I fill you up. Big hard cock going deeper inside your tight potato pussy pleasure pond. A sea of stars erupting as you're filled up. I love your pussy. Wet and soft and tight and mine. Going deeper inside. You kissing me hard as we fuck. Pinning you against the wall. Biting your ear. Mouth opening. Spitting. "You're a good girl," I tell you. You smile and open again. I spit. Slap your face. You close your eyes as I pick you up. Pinned against the wall. Sliding up and down my wet hard cock. "Cum for me butter baby," I tell you. "Cream on my cock." Your eyes close as you bite your bottom lip and breathe deeper. Legs wrapped around me. Cock deep in your tight pussy. Choked against the wall. Pinning you. Fucking you. Touching your clit. Cumming for me like a good girl. "Cream for me," I tell you again. You barely get out, "I am potato daddy." Moaning loud and losing control as you cum on my cock. Wrapping yourself around me. Water pouring down. Kissing hard. Creaming and dripping butter on me. I love you cumming on my cock. I pick you up and carry you to your room. Your cum dripping down my cock and balls. Soaking wet. Dripping on the floor. Our secret. It's curfew. Your friends would freak. You're a bad girl doing this. I want to see you sucking. I throw you on the bed and you jump to your knees. My hard cock waiting for you. Looking at yourself in the mirror. You sexy fucking potato. You look like a young nun. Sister O' Brien. She grew up to be a wench in her older years but a hot young nun. She would beat me with the bible. Loved it. You're sucking my cock as we look at you in your bedroom mirror. You're a good girl. I choke your neck as you spit on it. Licking it off my balls. Waving your ass in the air. I turn you around and bend you over. Filling you up from behind. Fucking you hard. Slapping that ass red. Your friends have no clue what a dirty little deviant girl you are. The silent one. It's the hottest. I'm going to cum in you. "Cream for me you hot fuck." I get you on the floor on your back. Legs wrapped around me. Choking you as I fuck you. Looking at you over your head in the mirror. You sexy fuck. Lifting up your back as you cum again for me. Spitting in your mouth. Cumming with you. Shooting hard. Police driving by. Sirens going off. Cumming hard inside. You're fucking soaking wet. I pull out and you open your mouth. My cum on your lips and face. Dripping on your perky tits. Your perfect nipples. Watching you lay there like a pleased potato. Lying on the floor. Licking and tasting my cum. A creamy potato. A little buttery baby. Stroking my cock. Malibu is burning. Police are rioting. Black people are dying. It's sad. So sad. But fuck me pink. I would take a bus for you all day. Four fucking buses. Hot potato pussy.

MILKY PLUM PUSSY

It's Wednesday. I think. I no longer care. This bullshit is never ending. Malibu is burning. American fucks won't wear masks. Corona is here for life. And I've spent the day working on my visa application. It's sad. So sad. So harny. The rules have changed now because of corona. Happy fucking days. Wear a mask you dumb fucks. I've been pissed all day. You've been working out. Looking like a hot little ferret fucker. Dressed in all black and body looking savage. Like hot dominatrix in Lululemon. I go for a stroll to clear my head. I can't keep filling out forms. Need some fruit. Maybe a plum. Love a nice plum. I spoke to my priest earlier about the situation but he didn't help. Father Tim, the harniest man alive. Kept interrupting me to tell me how hot the women on TikTok are. Very harny. Easy now, Father Tim. Reminded me of his father, Father Tim senior who was my priest when I was young. He loved to tell me how harny he was too as he walked me into the forest for a stroll. Can't remember much about them but even now I love a good stroll. I leave you doing yoga stretches and head out. You hot ferret fuck. Your body has had me turned on for days and weeks and too long. Non stop. Just hard all the time, like an Irish pikey after a bag of Stella. Hard as fucking nails. I'm strolling and looking up TikTok. I keep seeing a teenager crying on it. Fake crying. As you do. He's my new hero. I remember crying on the strolls with Father Tim Sr. now that I think of it. He always had my head buried in pines. I spot four good plums at Ralph's. I'm going to plum you up. You text me asking to get you some marshmallows and jalapeños. Who the fuck eats that. You really are a ferret. I tell you to be waiting on the bed on your hands and knees when I get back. "Yes, Father," you reply. I eat one plum on the stroll home. They're juicy as fuck. Lovely red sheen. It'll be like your ass soon enough. I walk in and your workout station has been abandoned. Good girl. You're on the bed. Wearing your red lingerie. You remind me of my childhood hero, Chris de Burgh, who sang Lady In Red. He loved wearing red lingerie too, the filthy whure. I walk to the bed and put the bag next to you. You're looking straight ahead. Eyes on the headboard. You're a good girl. Your skinny body looks sexy, a milky delight. "I bought you a cake as a treat," I tell you. "Thank you, Father," you reply. I take the chocolate cake out of the bag and place it on your back. "Don't let it fall," I tell you. You stay still. I rub your ass and spank a cheek. You bite your lip. I rub and spank again harder. You moan and bite more. The cake doesn't move. I spank ridiculously hard and you flinch. Cake stays on. Good girl. I take a plum out of the bag and you instinctively open your mouth. Good girl, you little milky ferret fucker. I kiss you first and pull your hair. Your mouth open. I spit it in. You smile and your eyes light up. I squeeze your neck as I climb onto the bed, kneeling in front of you. You undo my jeans and take my hard cock in your mouth. Spitting on it and licking the spit off. You're a hot little slut. You spit again and again. My cock is dripping wet and rock hard. Slippery as fuck, like a McDonald's floor. You rub my cock off your lips and gums, like the sweetest Irish cocaine. I fuck your mouth, hands on your back, rubbing your ass. Cake is still in the same place. Good girl. I spank your ass cheek hard and feel your pussy. You're soaking, like a mother's cheek at her son's funeral. I fuck your mouth hard until I hear you gag, reminds me of the U.S. immigration office fucking me with their never ending fees and rule changes. Your spit dripping down my balls. I'm going to plum you up. I get off the bed and put a plum in your wet mouth. Slap your face and you smile. I stand behind you and slide a plum inside your tight wet pussy. You're a hot fucking ferret. Your clit is swollen and throbbing. I start to rub it and tease you, plum juice dripping down your chin as you bite down. I slap your ass and spread your cheeks. Slowly slide the smallest plum inside your tight little asshole. As I slide it in and rub your clit, your body starts shaking. You're cumming on the plum, you little plum cummer. I rub on your clit as you cum hard, your arms and knees shaking, back quivering. You're trying but you can't. The cake falls off. Bad girl. You turn and look at me with frightened eyes. Plum in your ass. Plum in your mouth. I place the cake on the bed in front of you. "Put your face in the cake," I tell you. You do as you're told as I get on the bed and kneel behind you. Slowly sliding my hard cock inside your tight wet plum pussy. Filling you up as your face is buried in cake and plum. Reminds me of my stroll with Father Tim Sr., my face in the pines and dirt as he tried to drive the devil out of me. Feel like a round peg in a young boy's square hole. I slowly fuck you from behind and rub your clit as I feel you cum again.

Squirting on my cock like a cow in a midsummer heat. Fuck me. I love you cumming. You're a hot milky plum fuck ferret, as my Mum would say. Lovely lady. Malibu is burning. The fucking masks. Me visa. It's sad. So sad. But at least we have plums. And you have cake. So harny.

HOT LOAF

It's Friday. I do believe. Taylor Swift Day. Thank God. Things have been bleak. Malibu is burning. Corona is on fire. Britney is being held captive. Free Britney. For the love of God. It's sad. So sad. But at least I just did a podcast. Thank God. Again. It was complete rambles and shambolic but better than nothing. The drifting. The vagueness. The nothing of it all. I walk into the bedroom and you're naked. The nothing of it all. Sweet Jesus. You've the hottest body I've ever seen. And I've seen like, three hot bodies. At least. Yours is unreal. Like Mona and Lisa fucked and made this sexual deviant delight of a fuck body. Nicer than a bowl of broccoli cheddar soup. So nice. A gentle soup. So brave. You're looking at me, mouth open. Rubbing your pussy with your vibrator. Looks like a golden microphone. Makes me miss stand-up. So sad. Reminds me of my Uncle Pascal back in Ireland. He would always be on the microphone at the local school discos telling everyone to have a good time. Licking the microphone almost, he would get so excited. He taught me how to lick a microphone at school one time. In the dark cloakroom closet. Lovely uncle. Very gentle. You're moaning looking at me. I'm hard. Stripping naked at the bottom of the bed. Stroking looking at you. Watching you touch your hard nipples. Hearing the vibrator against your wet pussy. Your boobs like two mountains. Your pussy like a wet marsh. Reminds me of Glendalough back home. Uncle Pascal took me for a hike to the mountains one time. He taught me how to lick a microphone in the tall reeds in the marsh while we were there. So weird, he always had his microphone with him. Your mouth opens more as you pant and moan. Stomach breathing harder. I fucking love your stomach. Boobs going up and down, like two loaves of bread on the back of a bike on an old cobbled road. Bouncing and heaving along. Stroking my ponder pipe as your pleasure pond gets soaking wet. Watching you press your vibrator against your pussy. Tapping your clit. "Good girl," I tell you. "You like that, Daddy?" you ask. "I do, you hot potato fucker." You always tell me I give you Daddy issues. Purely because your Dad has issues with me and isn't a fan. I climb on the bed staring at your mouth. You're moaning harder and harder. Vibrator pressing against your swollen clit. My hand on your neck squeezing. Your beautiful boobs in the air, like hopes and dreams and a runaway balloon. You start cumming as I squeeze your neck harder. Pussy squirting on the bed. Eyes rolling like the fields of Kerry. Getting faint like you're back on heroin. Sucking my cock with your sexy wet mouth. Spitting on it as you climb to your hands and knees. Watching you in the mirror. Kneeling in front of your perfect ass in the air. Sucking on my cock like it's your last request. There's a stick of butter on the table next to the bed. You've been eating butter again. Bad girl. At least it's Kerrygold. I slap your ass and tell you to turn around. Your perfect loaf of an ass. You're a hot loaf. You're on your hands and knees facing the headboard. I rub the butter off your ass and pussy. Dripping in cum and Kerry's finest, just like Jesus wanted. You Kerrygold fucker. My tongue in your butter ass. Deeper as you moan. Running to your wet butter pussy. Licking it like it's a spoon of broccoli cheddar soup. Tasting your clit like it's French onion soup. My tongue sliding inside your tight butter pond and teasing you. Licking and tasting. Pressing your g-spot as you shake on the bed. Your butter ass loving my tongue as I rub your clit. Cumming pure butter gold for me. I spread butter on my cock like it's a potato at noon. Lay on the bed and you climb on top. Taking my cock and sliding it deep inside. Your marsh pit of joy. Your mountains in my face. Bouncing as you ride me. The sound of your wet pussy in the air. Like a flute tooting its own horn. Kissing and biting on your nipples. Reminds me of Uncle Pascal. Deep in the reeds. My cock filling up your tight pussy. Slapping that ass and squeezing your neck. Two of us lost down a mountain path. Cumming deep inside you. Shooting again and again as I grab you tight. Sucking on my fingers as we keep fucking. As you keep riding. As the butter drips out your ass. Malibu is burning. Poor Britney. The masks. It's sad. So sad. But fuck me pink. You're a hot cunt of a loaf.

PEACH PIGEON PUSSY

It's Wednesday. Midnight. The Lord's day. The devil's hours. Malibu is burning. Portland is on fire. Covid killed stand-up. It's sad. So sad. But fuck me pink you look hot tonight. You were mowing your garden all day. Taking photos in a mirror on the grass. Finding a new dark filter on your iPhone. You're sweaty and hot and delightful. Like eating a chicken leg at the beach. Now you're working out with me in your living room. I'm on your bike, sweating like a whure. You're on your yoga mat doing abs exercises. Like a true denim wearing, tree hugging, earth loving, slow fashion kind of creep. You remind me of my old priest Father Terry Wogan, he was like that too. Lovely man, Father Terry. He would take me for strolls down the church garden and push me into bushes, then grope and fondle as he helped me back out. Lovely man. Tender touch. Loving grope. Like you. You're in a white t-shirt and black thong, your favourite workout outfit. Your ass looks like a fucking peach, James would be proud of it. I can't stop staring as I cycle on the bike. Sweat dripping off me as I watch you stretch and defy gravity. How the fuck is your body this savage. You catch me creeping and walk to the bike. Facing me as you slide between my legs. Feeling my hard cock in my shorts as we kiss. Two sweaty creeps. I take your top off and then mine. Your sweaty savage body between mine and the handle bars. Stroking my ponder pipe as I feel your nipples getting harder for me. Kissing you hard as I pull you to me. Your tits against my chest. Squeezing your neck as you close your eyes. Stroking my cock as I slide your black thong off. Naked between my legs. You slide my shorts off and lick my cock, like a glorious ice cream on an 88 degree day. Spitting on it and stroking as you bend down and start sucking. Like a young Father Terry, pleasuring in the bushes. I hold your hair back as you spit and lick more. Looking at me in the eye as your tongue slides up and down, then taking me fully in your mouth. Sucking and slurping, like a calf at dinner time. I'm sitting on the saddle and your ass is pushing against the handlebars. Feeling your nipples as you suck. Hand on your back and pushing you down further. Hearing you gag and spit dripping off your chin. You come up for air like a dolphin in the Kerry rain and look at me. I kiss your wet dolphin lips and pull you close. My hard wet cock against your hot tight body. Squeezing your neck as I rub your clit. Feeling your wet dolphin pussy. You're soaking wet like a good girl. I pull your hair back as I kiss your hard nipples. Sucking and teasing as I feel your tight wet pussy. Feel likes a wet June gloom. Heavy and throbbing. Waiting to burst. I turn you around and bend you over the handlebars. Your James and the savage peach ass in the air. Spreading your cheeks and licking your ass. Teasing my tongue on your throbbing clit. Feeling you gush and pour like a drunk bartender in my mouth. Your peach pussy dripping down my chin. Reminds me of Father Terry and his love of me berries. I spread your ass and slide my tongue in, then run it along your heavy clit. You're moaning hard and ass pushing back against me. Like a pigeon in the night, my tongue is sliding in and out faster and faster. Tongue deep down your pleasure pond well. Pressing on your clit and spanking your ass. Body shaking as I get your g-spot and feel you cumming. You're a good peach pigeon pussy girl. Cumming for me. Soaking and dripping down your thighs. I stand up and slide my hard cock inside you. Grabbing your hair and slapping your ass. Fucking you hard on your handlebars, like a good moustache. Your creamy pussy feels amazing on my cock. Squeezing your neck and pulling your hair. Kissing your mouth over your shoulder as I go deeper and deeper. I press on your clit as my cock gets harder, deeper inside you. You moan and sweat as your body tenses for me. Cumming on my cock as I spank you hard. I grab your hair as I cum with you, deep inside your wet Gollum cave. You precious fucker. Malibu is burning. Stand up is dead. The world's on fire. It's sad. So sad. So harny. So sad. But fuck me pink. You're the hottest fucker alive.

STUNNING SALMON

It's Thursday. The day of St. Paul. A slow hot day. My brain has been lethargic as fuck. I must accept I'll now just be tired every day for the rest of my life. Malibu is burning. Someone opened a door in my face. Stand-up is dead. I'm losing my mind. It's sad. So sad. But I get back from a run and you're looking unreal. The hottest fucker. You were working out at home. Wearing a weighted vest. Reminded me of my Uncle Jimbo. He always wore vests and would give me hugs all sweaty. Hate when he climbed into my bed and hugged me. Sweat coming out of all of him. I was only five. It was a small bed. But you look hot sweating. In your black top and black yoga pants. Your boobs look unreal dripping wet with sweat, like two snowy mountains melting in the summer sky. Sweat dripping down you like a melon about to burst. I'm hard looking at you. At your neck. You've the finest neck. I want to pin you down on the carpet and squeeze your neck and kiss your sweaty body. But I must move your plants into your bedroom first. Onto your new shelves. Your cat has been eating the plants outside. So now your bedroom is a plant heaven. With your purple light. I want you naked. I hear the door and tell your cat no. But it's you. You finished working out. Your once perfect bun is now hanging to the side. You sweaty hot fucker. "Your plants are safe now," I tell you. I turn around and you're behind me. Looking at me in the mirror. Rubbing my cock through my black shorts. I kiss your lips and put my hand on your neck. You close your eyes and smile. I undo your bun and let your glorious hair fall down. Fuck me pink. You're the hottest fucker ever. Kissing your lips as I squeeze your neck. You stroking my hard cock. Reminds me of Uncle Jimbo. He would get me to sleep hugging me the same way. I kiss your lips and neck, down to your sweaty boobs. Taking your top off over your head. Kissing your snowy glorious mountains and licking your hard nipples. You fucking weapon. Kissing your stomach and pulling down your yoga pants. Your sweaty thighs in my face as I kiss them and your sexy pussy. Teasing you as I pull your pants off your feet. Standing up as you strip me naked. My top over my head. Sliding off my shorts. Getting on your knees and kissing my hard cock. Licking my balls and cock. Spitting on the head and taking it whole in your mouth. Swallowing it to the back of your throat. Gagging and pulling out, your spit covering my ponder pipe. Like a drunk priest serving Holy Communion. You stroke my cock and suck my balls, looking up at me while I pull your hair back in a pony tail. Fuck, your mouth feels unreal. Watching you touch yourself as you suck and spit. I want to taste you. I come behind you and get on my knees too. Bending you forward on your hands and knees in the mirror. Ass in the air and face on the ground. Hands on your back and spanking your ass. Kissing your sexy ass cheeks and spreading your legs. My tongue sliding between your tight wet pleasure pond. Feeling you gush in my mouth as I eat you out from behind. Tongue going deeper inside your sexy pussy. Rubbing your clit and your ass. Sliding my tongue from one to the other. Pressing on your clit as I finger you from behind. Teasing my cock against you. Your pussy tightening as I find your g-spot. Feeling you breathe deeper and deeper as your body tightens and then cums hard. Squirting on my hand and the floor. The poor floor. Like a drunk harny priest who spilled a glass of wine. I slide my hard cock inside your soaking pussy. Fucking you from behind in front of the mirror. Watching your face of pleasure and joy. You're so beautiful it's insane. Spanking your ass cheeks. Red. Squeezing your neck. Watching you in the mirror. Watching me. Mouth open. Like a stunning salmon. Leaping up the river. Your pussy gushing on me. My cock going deeper. Hitting your g-spot. Squeezing on your neck as we cum together. Shooting deep inside. Fucking you deeper and deeper. Like a riddle gone wrong. Sweaty bodies. Grabbing your hair. Pulling it back as I cum inside you again. Still hard and cumming. Your mouth open. Pulling out as you turn around and put your tongue out. Like a priest waiting for holy communion. Cumming again on your tongue as you swallow and suck. Fucking your sexy mouth as I stay hard. Your ass and pussy in the mirror. The two are most unreal. Your neck. Fuck me, your neck. Malibu is burning. My poor nose. Stand-up is dead. Me lost mind. It's sad. So sad. But fuck me stupid, I love your fine neck. You hot delight.

ABSOLUTE FUCKING DELIGHT

It's Wednesday. The day of our Lord. When Jesus goes to work. When St. Martin does his thing. You know the one. Biden smelled some hair. The heat is too much. I'm sweating. Malibu is burning. It's sad. So sad. But at least I got some writing done. I'm dizzy from it all. You've been in the bedroom working all day. On your OnlyFans. You made a grand already. You hot delight. I made zero. You're the bread winner now. Very handy. I'm going to take you for dinner. I knock on the door. You're in your giant Coors t-shirt talking to some guy online about feet. I like it. I like your face. You're the hottest fucking woman I've ever seen. It's a bit insane. You fucking delight. You finish up and swing around on your chair. "I miss my chicken," you tell me. "Huh?" I'm dizzy from not eating. I'm sweating because of your smile. Your eyes light it up. It makes me dumb. "My chicken, Rainbow. I miss her." Oh yeah. Your chicken back home. "Are you on drugs?" I ask. "No, but we should try mushrooms." "OK, I'm down." Thank God you didn't say meth. And anal. Or pegging. I'm hungry and weak. Your eyes fuck me up. "Let's go eat," I tell you. You strip off your t-shirt and stand in front of me, naked. For fuck's sake. "What do you want to eat?" you ask. Fucking you. I move the hair out of your face and look at you. What a beautiful bastard. I kiss your lips and watch you close your eyes. Naked and delightful. I pull you closer and kiss you hard, biting on your beautiful lip. Your head rolls back as I pull away, hand on your neck, hearing you breathe deeper. I squeeze your neck tighter. Your hand opening my belt. Kissing your chin, down your body, squeezing your neck tighter again as I kiss your hard nipples. Biting on them slightly as I hear you moan. You hot fuck. I kiss your lips and you open your eyes. The hottest fucker. Looking at me as you undo my belt. Jeans falling down. Your hand on my hard cock as I feel your swollen clit. Like an eye after a bad schoolyard beating. Throbbing and joy. Reminds me of the beatings by my old teacher and priest, Father Terry O'Shea. Lovely man but awful temper. Used to beat both my eyes. Then caress me tenderly in his office after. I hold no grudges. Taught me how to pleasure myself, one of the best gifts you can give a boy. My cock is hard as a rock as you play with the head, getting to your knees and licking it slowly. Looking up at me like an altar boy trying his best, like a butcher boy giving it socks, like a carpenter working some tender loving wood. Fun childhood in Ireland. You spit on my cock and lick my balls. I run my hands through your blonde hair, reminds me of Father Terry. Your wet mouth on my cock like a drunken homeless man guzzling a beer. Fucking Christ, guzzle on. It's like I go down a hole of delight in the sky when you're sucking me. "Do you like that?" you ask. I can't think straight. I love your mouth. My brain is telling me your face is like a beautiful door to a castle but it doesn't make any sense. I'm dumb now. "Your face is like a door," I tell you. "Mmhmmm," you reply. You know I'm dumb. I squeeze your neck lightly as you suck. You pause and enjoy it. You want it harder. I squeeze more as your spit is on my cock. You have me as dumb and as hard as a rock. You need air. I let go and you breathe hard and smile. "Get on the bed," I tell you. You climb on on your hands and knees, looking over your shoulder. You sexy fuck. I slap your ass cheek, hard. It rings out in the air, like a young Filipino choir singing a Christmas carol. I spank again. The second chorus. I spank harder again. Your ass is red. We must make it like a rainbow. For Rainbow. I spank hard and hear you moan. Your pussy drenched. Your clit throbbing. Your ass in the air. I'm glad you didn't ask me to peg. I get behind you and tease your pussy with my cock. You're dripping, it's like a pleasure pond. I slide my cock inside and hear you moan louder. You hot chicken fuck. My hands on your back. On your neck. Pulling your hair. Fucking you deep from behind. You rubbing your clit. You're a good fucking girl. Spanking you harder as you moan louder and louder. Pulling you up on just your knees. Rubbing your clit and squeezing your neck as you slide up and down my hard cock. You're the hottest fucking delight. Pushing you down onto the bed. Your face in the pillow. Me on top. Feeling your pussy tighten. Watching your face as you cum for me. Like a good fucking girl. Squeezing your neck and deep inside of you. Cumming for me as I start to cum with you. Shooting deep inside. Sweating on sweating. Cumming and fucking. Jesus Christ. You're the best. Your face in the pillow. Turning to the side. Smiling at me. Pulling out as I cum on your back. You smiling even more. Jesus. Your smile. Malibu is burning. I'm fucking sweating. Biden is smelling. But sweet Lord. You fuck. Thank fuck you didn't say meth, you absolute fucking delight.

LITTLE HOT CHICKEN HEN

It's Thursday. The Lord's Sabbath. St. Hippolytus Day. Lovely man. Stern priest. Died in prison. As we all should. It's roasting out. Malibu is burning. There's a lake on fire. Stand-up is dead. It's sad. So sad. But I'm reading my book. The Tao of Pooh. About Winnie the Pooh. And Taoism. Or something. I'm on the couch. Trying to read. Distracted. You walk in. That's why. You fuck. You left earlier for a casting. Looking like the high end model you are. In your cropped black top, slightly baggy high waisted jeans and fake snakeskin boots. Jesus you're a fucking delight every day. But I couldn't concentrate because I've wanted to strip you naked and fuck you since you walked out the door. "How was the casting?" I ask. "Delightful and breezy," you reply. Swanning in the door to the bedroom, like a deviant swan at midnight. You have the confident strut of my Uncle Jerry, how he would stumble and strut into my room drunk when I was young. Climb into bed and tell me magic stories with his magic wand. Fond times. You come out of the bedroom changed. Yellow tank top, yellow shorts, yellow socks. I fucking love you in yellow. "You look like a chicken," I tell you. "Thanks," you smile. It's hot out. You're horny. I can tell. "It's hot," you tell me. "I know," I reply. "I'm horny." "I know," I say again. "Will you read to me?" you ask. "Maybe." "I'll suck your dick." Okay. Uncle Jerry used to use the same trick on me, a sucker from a young age. "Get the eggs," I tell you. Your eyes light up. You love the eggs game. You little hot hen. You return from the kitchen with two eggs. Standing in front of me. Leaning down to kiss me. Your fucking lips. That fucking smile. You stand up and take off your top. I love your body. Better than any religious excursion. Slide your shorts down your long legs. Naked in front of me. Just in your yellow socks. Getting on your knees and opening my belt. "Read for me." I start to read as you take my hard cock out of my jeans. "There once was a bear named Pooh- Wait. The eggs." Your eyes smile. You take an egg and slowly slide it inside your wet pussy. "Both of them." You do as you're told. You're a good girl. A nice little chicken hen. "Don't break them." "I won't, Father," you tell me. I go back to reading. "There once was a bear named Pooh." Your mouth on my hard cock. Spitting and watching it slide down to my balls. Stroking it slowly as you look at me. Your blue eyes. I forget to read watching you. Slapping your face gently. You smile and start licking the spit off my cock. Kissing the head and deepthroating it. "Oh fuck me, Pooh," I say by mistake. "Keep reading," you tell me, coming up from gagging to get air. "There once was a bear named Pooh... Jesus fucking Christ... and he believed in the power of Tao." I fling the book across the room as you gag on my cock again. Grabbing your hair and forcing you down more. Better that Uncle J any day of the week. A toothy man. You come up for air smiling, spit on your chin, stroking my cock and looking at me. You hot fucking hen. "Get on the table," I tell you. You do as you're told.

Like a good girl. Climbing on the dining table and laying on your back. The eggs are still inside your wet pussy. Still intact. You start touching yourself as I strip naked. Standing between your legs. Pulling you towards me. Watching you rub your clit for me. Hand on your neck. Squeezing. Pinching your nipple. You open your mouth and I spit inside. You hot fuck. Slap your face as you moan louder and louder. Legs clenching on me. You're close to cumming. I can feel your thighs shaking. Don't break the eggs. Right before you cum I grab your hand and hold it down on the table. Choking you. Teasing your clit. Your eyes pleading to cum. Not yet. "Are you a good girl?" You nod yes. I let go of your hand. You rub your clit again and start to cum hard. Hand on your neck choking you. Cumming for me like a good girl. The eggs pop out and land on the table. Wet and ready. Good girl. You look at me and smile. I pull you closer to me and slide my hard cock inside your tight warm pussy. Your eyes light up and mouth opens moaning. I pin you to the table by your neck as I fuck you deeper and deeper. Slapping your ass as your legs wrap tighter around me. Grabbing your hair and slapping your face. You're a hot messy fuck. Like a drunk Irish man trying to walk up a wet hill. Sliding up and down my hard wet cock. Your back arches and legs tighten on me as you cum again. I feel your pussy tighten as I cum with you. Shooting deep inside. Choking you harder. Spanking you hard. Pulling out and cumming on your beautiful body. Malibu is burning. Stand up is dead. There's a lake on fire. It's sad. So sad. But at least we have eggs for lunch, you hot fucking chicken hen.

BLUE EYED FUCK

It's Sunday. The Lord's day. The black Sabbath. I'm driving home from Mass. Such a lovely sermon. Father Ben Jerry winked at me while feeding my Holy communion. Put his fingers in my mouth for ten seconds too. Bit odd. Malibu is burning. I'm hungover. I was fingered by a priest. It's sad. So sad. But you texted me a video asking if I liked your new red lipstick. You look fucking savage. Like a young duck on a sunny dawn. I almost crashed driving, you looked that hot. I love red lipstick now. My Aunt Bernice used to wear it when I was young. She loved to kiss me on the lips. Had a lovely moustache for a woman. I get home and you're in the kitchen. Sipping on a Whiteclaw. You hand me one as I walk in and kiss your fucking face. Your red fucking lips. Jesus Christ. I drop the Whiteclaw and kiss you harder. It's Sunday and a holy day but sweet Jesus you have me hard as a fucking kite. In your black backless top and white shorts. I unbutton and slide them off. You undo my belt and my jeans are off. We're naked in the kitchen. You in your black thong. Me in my pink one. I pick you up and bring you to the bedroom. Flop you on the bed like a sack of potatoes. You hot fucking Sunday spud. I want you with gravy. You lean forward and take my cock in your mouth. Your ass in your thong like the American dream. Licking my cock slowly as your blue eyes look up at me. Sweet Jesus you're beautiful. Stroking my cock as you suck my balls. Piercing me with your dagger eyes. Same look Father Ben Jerry gave me when he fingered me. My hands on your back as you deep throat me. Gagging on my cock. You pull it out and spit on it. "You've a really smooth cock," you tell me. "Thank you," I say, too turned on and dumb. "It's like marble," you tell me. "Thank you," I dumbly reply again. I get on the bed and get on top of you. Looking at those eyes. They're dazzling with delight. I put my hand on your neck and squeeze. You leave out a devilish deviant moan. It's my favourite. Biting your lip and smiling with your eyes. I slide your thong down your legs and watch as you start rubbing your clit. You're a good girl. Looking at me as you touch yourself. Squeezing your neck slightly harder. You open your mouth and I spit inside. Watch it on your tongue. I lean down and you spit it back in mine. We have covid now. I kiss you hard. It's like being lost in a dream. Stupid and dumb and horny and hard. That's how you make me. Teasing my cock along your wet pussy as you keep rubbing your clit. Your mouth opening as you look at me. Moaning and breathing deeper. "Fuck me," you tell me. "Not yet." I want to see you cum. My marble dick teasing your soaking pussy. Your legs start quivering as I squeeze your neck. "Good girl," I tell you. You start to cum while looking at me in the eye. It's fucking beautiful. I slide my cock inside your tight pussy, eyes still locked. Like a drunk man trying to look at his phone. You cumming on my cock as I pin you to the bed. Fucking you deeper. Your tight pussy dripping wet. Kissing your beautiful mouth. Spitting and spanking. Your sexy red lips. Sweating and fucking. Looking at you in the big double mirror as we fuck. Eyes locked on each other in the mirror. You've ruined mirrors for me. I get turned on every time I see one now. Thinking of how you look naked in one. You get on your hands and knees as I fuck you from behind. Watching you. Your savage body. My cock deep inside. Spanking your ass. Your poor red right ass cheek. Taking a battering. Grabbing your hair and pushing your face into the pillow. You turning to the side. Mouth open. Waiting for my spit. You sexy fuck. We have covid now. I turn you around as we fuck slowly. Looking at each other. It's intense and hot as fuck. Like Father Ben feeding me a wafer on a summer's day. I squeeze your neck as you start to cum again. You're a good girl. I love you cumming for me. I pin you down and start cumming inside you. Shooting hard. Kissing your lips. Looking at your beautiful blue eyes. Sweet Jesus. You're the best. "Let me taste." Hot fuck. You get on your knees and start sucking the cum off my cock. Looking at me. Like a nun in heat. Praying for forgiveness. Malibu is burning. You ruined mirrors. I was fingered. It's sad. So sad. But fuck me pink. Look at your fucking eyes.

FUNERAL EYES

It's Wednesday. Pump day. The day of St. Francis, a gentle pope. We're going to the beach. Malibu is burning. Republicans are doing coke on TV. Someone stole my mail. It's sad. So sad. But at least we can jump in the ocean. Thanks, Jesus. You show up wearing white runners, black jeans and a backless snake skin top. What kind of fucking beach wear is this? I think to myself.

Hmm. "What kind of fucking beach wear is this?" I ask you out loud. "I'm coming from a casting," you retort, like a true model feck. Oh yeah. I forgive you. I've been worried all morn about you making me hard on the beach. Which shorts to wear. Maybe jeans. It's been stressful. Luckily I remembered an old masking tape trick my old priest Father Billy O' Shaughnessy taught me when I was young. He would take me around the back of the church where the goats would hang and show me how to tape down a hard ponder pipe. One layer of masking tape usually worked but sometimes two were needed. Then he would have me rip them off. "The pain," he would say, "the pain and joy of it all," ruffling my hair while his penis bled. Lovely man. Your eyes are distracting me as we drive west. Towards burning Malibu. They're blue and brilliant and as bold as a nun in warm pub after three whiskeys. Those nuns do get frisky. I feel the masking tape budge on my ponder pipe. I only used one layer to tie it down. Should've went with two. "Did you tape down your dick again?" you ask me. "I did," says I. We're stuck in traffic. You stick your hand down my shorts and smile. I'm as hard as a kite in a sheet of hail. You tug my shorts down as I drive. I keep my mind on my old sheep Tessie, trying to stay focused. You unbuckle your belt and spit on my masked up cock. "You've a very smooth penis," you tell me, "It's like a marble delight." "Thank you," I reply, cordially, thinking of Tessie and trying not to crash. As I picture myself kneeling in front of Father Billy you yank hard on the masking tape. Sweet mother of Christ. Mary. Fucking Mary. I scream, internally. And then again, externally. Before the pain sets in you spit on my cock and start sucking. Your savage tongue licking my hard cock and lips kissing my stunning balls. Massaging them as you take all my cock in your mouth. Looking at me with your blue funeral eyes as you suck. The thought of death makes me smile, imagine never having to do laundry again. Fuck, I'm too turned on. You keep sucking as I drive down the PCH, code for something potato related no doubt. One hand on your back as I steer wildly down the highway. Motorway. Freeway. Free fucking way. I can barely see. Sand in my eyes as I drive. Your wet mouth sucking my hard cock. Feels like a waterfall of joy is pouring over me. Like a lump of mash being covered in gravy. "Cum inside me," you tell me, like a devil would say. "Okay," I reply, lost in your world of deviant delight and deceit. I pull in on the potato highway and rip your jeans off. You get on top of me, sliding my hard cock inside your tight, wet pleasure pond. Sweet Jesus. Sweet gravy. Pouring over my spud. Sliding you up and down my cock as I kiss and lick your nipples. Hands on your perfect ass as you bounce on me, like Jesus to a child, as George Michael would say. I rub your clit as you slowly grind on me. Looking at your blue funeral eyes. I pull your face towards me. Kissing your wet lips. Spitting in your mouth. Taking the spit back again. Please wear a mask. Kissing you hard again. You slowly grinding on me. Head hitting the roof. Cock deep inside. Peeling back as you start to cum on me. Like an orange. I pull you closer as you grind deeper and deeper. You sexy fuck. Your pussy gushing over me, like an eager priest ushering altar boys around the rear. I love fucking you by the beach. In the car. Your cum on me. Eyes looking at me. Spitting in my mouth. You sexy fuck. Your warm wet pussy tightens on my cock. I start to cum deep inside you, shooting hard. Thinking of Jesus. The stars. Potatoes. Cumming again. Kissing your lips. Your wet pussy on my wet cock. Sitting there breathing. You looking at me. Smiling. Hopping off back to the passenger side. Legs spread. Looking at me. Watching my cum drip out of your glorious pussy. Tasting and licking it off your finger. Malibu is burning. Me mail. My masking tape cock. It's sad. So sad. But fuck me, Father Billy was right. The joy of it all, you hot beach delight.

SHOE FULL OF JOY

It's Tuesday. The day of three-day-hangover. Malibu is burning. The air smells like a fiery sock. The Clippers choked. My stalker has stopped writing me poetry. It's sad. So sad. But at least we have Mass. Reminds me of you, a shoe full of joy. We went to a late sermon, Father Terry was hosting. Fine man, harny as sin but such a gentle touch with the Holy Communion. Reminded me of Father Gerry back in Ireland when I was growing up. Loved to stick a finger in my mouth as he was feeding me the body of Christ. I was 12, he was 54. Good times. Everyone at Mass was wearing their masks, it was good to see. Reminded me of the time we went to that orgy and they all had gimp masks on. They served us a Chinese buffet beforehand and then we all went to a room next door and the pumping began. You squirted on my cock in front of a crowd of 20. No one knew it was us but everyone loved your body the most. A fucking weapon. A dripping bucket of wet delight. I'm horny walking down the aisle coming back from communion. Father Terry's finger taste still in my mouth. Tasted like honey for some reason. You love honey. Licking it off my cock. Wet and sticky on your lips. Precum and honey, your favourite Sunday brunch. I join you back at the pew. Everyone is saying a silent prayer. On their knees. While my eyes are closed I feel your hand reach for my hard cock. Rubbing it through my jeans. At least I hope it's you. Maybe it's Father Terry. He reminds me of a character from the Derry Girls, loves to slap the shit out of people. I'm so hard and turned on now while being rubbed and praying. Sorry, Jesus. I open my eyes. It's you. Sorry, Terry. Your mask is covering everything but your eyes. Your eyes are dancing. You hot horny whure. You love the Derry Girls. You want church sex. I put my hand down your pants and feel your pussy from behind. We're on the last pew, it's okay. I hope. Your tight pleasure pond is soaking. Pulling your thong to the side as I feel how wet. Your clit swollen. Covering my fingers. Hearing you breathe deeper as I press on your clit. Breathing through your nose as you look at me. Rubbing each other. Two harny fuckers. We stand in unison and make our way to the old monk's bathroom. Lovely spot. Genuflect and bless ourselves with some holy water. You take my fingers and suck the holy water and pussy juice off them. Your mask is off. You need to cum. I close the bathroom door behind us, the lock doesn't work. There's honey on the sink. Good man, Father Terry. Reminds me of the time I fell in a swamp by the church back in Ireland.

Father Gerry took me to his chapel and showered me down. He said I was a lovely little naked honey fucker. I can't remember why he said that. He was on his knees scrubbing my knees and wiping me clean. Lovely man. You pull down your pants and get on your knees, handing me the honey bottle. You honey god. Opening your mouth for me. Undoing my jeans. Pouring honey into your open mouth. Tongue wide open. Eyes wide shut. I slap your face. You smile. Spit in your mouth. Body of Christ. You smile again and swallow. Good girl. Slapping my cock off your cheeks. You spit on it and stroke it slowly, looking at me in the eye. Like Peter did with Jesus. No denying that. Spitting on it again as you kiss my balls. Looking at me. For the love of Christ. Father Terry would be jealous. Your tongue darting along my balls like it's headed to the bullseye. You're like a wise old man down the pub about to hit 180. Stroking and sucking my cock with your honey lips and mouth. A boat of fucking sexy wonder at my feet. Fucking your mouth with my rock hard ponder pipe. The pied pumper leading the Merry way. Watching your pussy dripping as you kneel. Rubbing your clit as you fuck your mouth with my cock. Gagging and spit. Dripping and wet. Licking and precum. Cumming on your lips and face. Grabbing your hair and slapping your face. Cumming deep down your throat. You horny hot honey god. Swallowing my cum and keeping me rock hard. I stand you up and bend you over the toilet. Mother Mary staring down at us as I eat your pussy from behind. A soaking swamp of wet cum waiting to burst. Tongue in your ass. Along your lips. Biting your cheeks. Teasing your clit. Pressing on it, like a Scientology member pushing me to sign. Join the cult. Suck the cunt. Lick the ass. Making you cum. Your pussy exploding in my mouth. Cum dripping as you put on your mask. Muffle the moans. Save the corona. Honey juice running down your thighs. I stand up and slide my hard ponder pipe deep in your bog pond. Looking over your shoulder at me. Grabbing your neck. Pushing your face into the wall. Fucking you as cuck Mary watches on. Slapping your fine ass. There's a knock at the door. Is that you, Jesus? "Hang on, Father," I say, a murmured apology. The thought of someone entering is too much for you, cumming on my cock hard. I put my hand over your dirty whore mouth as I cum with you. Muffling the joy. So sad. Honey dripping. Your eyes pleading at me for more. You're a good girl. A good Derry's girl. I pull out and watch my cum drip out of your pussy. You hot fuck. I love your cream pie. You should be on a window sill. I tell you to shush and realise. You must leave through the window. Otherwise we'll go to hell. You do as you're told and climb out the window, falling into a bush. You did well. Cum still dripping. A knock at the door. Father Terry. I depart and he stops me by the end. He can smell it in the air. "Did you enjoy the honey?" he asks. I did, I tell him. "Five Hail Marys," he replies. He knows. Malibu is burning. Clippers choked. Stalker poetry is over. It's sad. So sad. But at least we weren't caught. No hell for us yet, you hot honey whore.

VANILLA ICE CREAM PUSSY

It's Wednesday. The day of Holy St. Paul. A pious man. A man like myself. Malibu is burning. The air smells like smoke. I stubbed my toe in the night. Fruit makes me sick. It's sad. So sad. But at least we decided to work out. Sweat out the woes. Running the streets. Even though the weather app says the air might kill us. Must stay in shape. That's what my old teacher Sister Lucy would tell me, as she pulled down my pants and slowly slapped my bare cheeks in school. "Must," spank, "stay," spank, "in shape," she would say. I never knew why. I never did anything wrong. But I was always raw. I'm trying to focus on the snap peas I have in my pocket as we run the streets. But you're making it hard. The hottest fucking wife. Dressed in all black. Black tank top and black booty shorts. Your hair in pig tails. Fuck me pink, you're a hot little honey pig. I want you doused in honey bacon. I'm rock hard running behind you. My hard cock trying to burst out of my shorts, like an extra from Shawshank Redemption. That was my Uncle Finnegan's favourite movie. He would put me up on his knees and bounce me up and down as we watched, alone, naked, in his isolated farmhouse. It was too hot for clothes, he would tell me. I didn't know any better, I was barely 8 at the time. Lovely uncle. He's dead now. I can barely run straight from looking at your body ahead of me. You're like a pig in its prime. Your body is a weapon, a war crime in 12 countries. We run past our favourite church, St. Paul's and stop for a break. I'm panting, like a whure in heat. You're just glistening, taking deep breaths, like a salmon that just leapt out of the water. You hot salmon fucker. "What?" you ask, while I stare at your lips. "I fucking want you right now," I tell you, taking you by the hand. We go through the bushes and the church shire like two horny hobbits, around to the back where no one can see us. It's dark. It's grand. You're wet. I'm hard. I stand you on the church steps so you're my height. "Hello hot fucker," I say, watching you bite your lip as I pull your shorts down. I want you naked on the church steps. Father Terry won't mind. I pull your shorts down and you take your tank top off. You're in your blue g-string and running shoes. Jesus Christ, you're like a vision from God. "Are you my good girl?" I ask you, hand on your neck, pulling you into me. "I am Daddy," you reply. I kiss your lips and pull you to me. We kiss hard, like a drunk horny aunt kissing me on my communion day. Ah, Aunt Bernice, lovely woman. Lovely wet lips. Your nipples are rock hard in the cold. I kiss your neck and body, licking your nipples and biting softly. You on your toes. Horny and getting wetter. My hand on your ass. Spreading your cheeks. Feeling the warmth of your wet pussy, like a warm bog on an Irish summer's day. I squeeze your neck again and you open your mouth as I spit in it. You smile and we kiss. I slap your beautiful face and you bite your lip harder. Reaching for my cock as I tell you, "Get on your knees." You do as you're told. You're a good wife. A hot salmon. Taking my cock out of my shorts as you spit on it and look up at me. Naked on the church steps. Like how Jesus would want it. Like how Uncle Finnegan would always want me. I miss him. You stroke your cock and look at me. I slap your face again harder. You smile and take my hard cock in your wet mouth. Like a diver entering a pleasure pond. My hard cock hitting the back of your throat as you deepthroat and gag on it. You sexy fuck. Sucking and spit and precum dripping down your chin. Onto your hot fucking tits. Rubbing them for me as I fuck your mouth. "Good girl, you're a good fucking girl." You moan as you suck my cock deeper and faster. I grab the back of your head as I'm about to cum. I think of Mother Mary and cum hard in your mouth. You moaning as I fill you up. Taking it out as your tongue wants more. Cumming on your face and tits. You taking it like a parishioner taking the body of Christ. I want your pussy. I pull you to me and watch you swallow. Smiling at me. You're a good girl. We kiss, you're as wet as a sock in a puddle. Your chin dripping. Your pussy soaking. Your tits honey fucked. "Turn around," I tell you. You do as you're told. Hands against the church door, like Martin Luther nailing his rules to a new religion. You lift your ass cheeks up for me as I pull your blue g-string down. Sweet Jesus your ass, I would give up four kids for it. The hottest wife. I spank your ass cheek hard and hear you moan. "You like that?" I ask, spanking again harder. "I do, Daddy," you moan. I spank again. Your ass cheek red. Your pussy dripping. I get on my knees and taste your pussy from behind. Tastes like vanilla ice cream, with a side of tea. My favourite. I slide my tongue up and down your clit as I hear you moan louder. Like a choir ready to burst. I want to tease you more. I take some snap peas out of my pocket and slide them inside your tight ass. You flinch and moan as I slide them in, nature's anal beads. Thanks, God. Feeling you get wetter in my mouth as I eat you out from behind. "Rub your clit," I tell you. You do as you're told, like a good flute. I kiss your ass cheeks and spread them wide. You have me so fucking hard with cum still dripping off my cock. I slowly eat your ass, sliding my tongue in and pulling the snap peas out. My tongue ducking your tight ass as you rub your throbbing clit, like a bloated Santa rubbing his belly. My tongue deep in your tight sexy ass, fingering your soaked pussy, pressing on your clit with you. I spit on your tight ass and my tongue slides deeper inside. Your thighs and legs slowly start to quiver and shake as you start cumming hard for me. Good girl. Banging the door and moaning loud as you cum in my mouth, dripping down your legs, my tongue sliding between your tight ass and throbbing clit. I stand up and pull your hair back. We kiss over your shoulder as my cock slides deep inside your wet sock pussy. Fucking hell you feel like heaven on a rainy day, pouring on my cock as I fuck you deep. Choking your neck from behind as we fuck hard against the church door. Only a barn door is better. I push you against it hard and fill your pussy up deeper. Choking your neck. Pulling your hair. "You're a good fucking girl," I tell you again. "Fuck me Father," you moan at me. I spank your ass red raw as you moan and cum for me again. Cumming on the church door. Like two horny mice. I cum inside your stormy pussy, seeing Jesus and thinking of Terry. Our bodies sweaty. Dirty sinful fuckers. You're the hottest fucking wife. Malibu is burning. The air is dying. My poor toe. It's sad. So sad. But fuck me dumb, you're my favourite hot horny nun wife whore. We should run some more.

GLORYHOLE HAND

It's Thursday. The day of St. Agnes, the horniest of all the saints. A lovely woman. Malibu is burning. The air is dead and dying. It's hard to breathe. I ate a bad pear earlier. Fuck fruit. It's sad. So sad. But at least we've been turning oursleves on all day. Sending each other half naked photos while we were running errands. You in your lingerie. Me hard in my shorts. Nothing turns me on more than you being turned on for me. Reminds me of my granduncle Timmy, he always said the same. Caressing my hair in the closet. Giving me four shillings to keep it a secret. I was naked and hard for you in a changing room early. I was so turned on, I bought four jackets. It's 98 degrees. What a dumb man. But what a great band. We're driving to LAX to pick up your friend who's visiting, Tammy. Sister Tammy, to be exact. She's a nun. An actual nun. I'm barely able to drive straight. Your lips are on my cock as I'm driving down La Cienaga. Sucking my hard cock. You beautiful fucker. Like a ferret sucking a stick in the mud. Loving life as you spit on my cock and smile at me. Stroking my cock with your butchered manicure hand. Your nails stuck to glue and you had to pull four off. Looks like a hand you'd see stick out of a gloryhole. The hand of someone with a gruff voice. Your lips back on my hard cock. Licking and spitting on it. I'm so fucking turned on. I can't even see or drive. I need to pull in. I have a place. I pull into a garage. It's a truck stop. There's a gloryhole. I saw it before. Perfect place for you. "Go around the back of the restroom," I tell you. You do as you're told. You're a good wife. I kiss your lips as I park the car. I go in the front, you around the back. I lock the restroom door and see the hole. Your gloryhole hand reaches through. Reaching for my hard cock. You take it and stroke it like a gruff trucker on a long haul. Gentle but firm. I stick my dick into the hole and hope for the best. Thank fuck, I don't feel a beard. It's you. Sucking my dick through a hole in the wall, just like how Jesus wanted. Reminds me of the cupboard with granduncle Timmy. All sorts of holes going on. I cum so quick. The rush of it all. I hear you laugh with cum in your mouth. You hot fucker. I wash up and go back to the car. You're sitting there waiting. Cum in your mouth. "Swallow it for me," I tell you. You do as you're told. We're back driving. I can see again. Rubbing your wet pussy as we drive. Your cunt like an overgrown cucumber. Juicy and ready to burst. Humans are like cucumbers with anxiety, is what granduncle Timmy would tell me in that cupboard. I never knew what he meant. He's dead now. You start to cum as I rub your throbbing clit, pulling into LAX. Reaching for the roof. Screaming muffled screams into my hand. We pull up and pick up Sister Tammy like nothing was going on. She's a hot nun. Even in her nun shawl. "What's that smell?" she asks. The car must smell of cum. "A pear?" I say, driving off. "Nice smelling pear," she replies. She has a glint in her eye. You can't help yourself and tell her everything. Sister Tammy smiles and is shocked. "Did you say your prayers?" she asks. "Not yet," I tell her. "We should all be on our knees," she says. She's horny. The hot nun. "Want to see where the glory be to God hole is?" I ask her. She bites her lip and nods yes. Hot Tammy. You smile next to me, biting your lip too. You hot fuckers. We pull into the truck stop and three of us go into the restroom. Surprisingly clean for a gloryhole place of God. You and Tammy start making out straight away. Reminds me of my next door neighbour Connie and her special friend Bernie growing up in Ireland. Two lonely farmers who I never realised were lesbians. I would see them in the muck all the time wrestling. Made sense. Tammy sits on the sink as you start to go down on her. I start kissing the nun and squeezing her neck. You start licking my cock and her pussy. Spitting on her clit and my body of Christ. I want to fuck your tight pussy again. I stand you up. You both start making out. I stand behind you and slide your shorts off, sliding my cock inside your tight wet pussy. You moan into the nun's mouth, like a ship moaning at a lighthouse on a wet night. My cock filling you up. Fucking you deep as you suck on her nipples. She opens her mouth and I spit in her, the blood of Christ. You looking over your shoulder at me. "You like that?" I ask. You nod. "Good fucking girl. You're a good girl, you sexy fuck." Your pussy tightens on my cock as I tell you. You turn around and sit on the sink. I slide my cock inside your soaking pussy again. It's like a carpet after I spilt a pint of water on it, brewing with cum. I choke your neck as I fill you up, sliding deeper and deeper. Playing with your hard nipples. They're like raisins on Christmas cake. Pulling on them softly. Kissing them and biting gently. You moaning. Tammy goes behind me and starts kissing me neck, down my back, on her knees, eating my ass. There's a nun eating out of my ass at a gloryhole truck stop. Thanks, God. You start to cum as I pull your nipples and choke your neck. The hottest fuck ever. Jesus. Your thighs. My favourite. Wrapped around me. Tammy's tongue in my ass as you cum on my cock. Sweet fucking Jesus. Where are the three wise men? I start to cum inside you deep as we kiss hard. Tongue to tongue and ass and tongue. Cumming hard. Like a good priest would. Malibu is burning. The air is dying. Pears are over. It's sad. So sad. But fuck me stupid, what a great manicure to keep us going. Thanks, superglue.

SUGAR CUM FAIRY

It's Friday. The day of St. Joseph, the local saint of splendour. Stunning jawline for a saint. Malibu is burning. Ruth Bader Ginsburg just died. TikTok is being banned tomorrow. It's sad. So sad. You've been wailing all day. You love TikTok. It gives you life, you say every day. I'm gutted too. I won't be able to see what my favourite celebrity maniac Devin Caherly is up to. I'll miss his tears. Those stunning tears. A sad day. You've been making some final tiktoks to lift the spirits. Dancing the WAP dance. You hot wet ass potato. Doing the splits and pounding the floor as you wail and cry. You look hot when you cry, like a potato coming out of the oven. You look even hotter in your outfit. Black booty shorts and black crop top hoodie with white tube socks. Now I'm harny and sad. The most deadliest combination. I need something to cheer me up. Plums. I need some plums. "I'll be back," I tell you, like a horny Terminator. You look up from the bedroom floor, tears in your eyes, "Please, don't leave me like TikTok." I hurry and get the plums. Horny as fuck thinking about you sad on the floor. Like a cat sprawled out, dreaming of killing a bird. I eat a plum on the walk back from the shop, so juicy and pure. Reminds me of Bishop Brennan, he used to call me that as he massaged my 11 year old buttocks after soccer training. He was the coach and I was his favourite. We would discuss tactics in the communal showers. Lovely man, great masseuse. Very strong hands. I walk in the door, plum juice dripping from my chin. You're doing a headstand, Usher is playing in the background. You're doing the splits upside down. You hot giraffe. Fuck. I want you naked. Covered in plum and cum. My sugar cum fairy. "Hi," you say, upside down. "You look fucking beautiful," I tell you. "Fuck me then," you say. "Don't move." I drop the bag of plums at your feet and take your socks off upside down. "Don't fall, or you're a bad girl," I tell you. "Yes, Father," you reply. I'm a priest now. I take your socks off and then slowly slide your shorts up your legs. Kissing your calves and thighs. Down to your ass. Kissing your cheeks. Running my tongue over your tongue. Taste your wetness through it, like a dog licking a wet bag of trash. I squeeze a plum over your thong to make it wetter. Kissing your thighs and ass cheeks and taste your plum thong. I love your thighs, they remind me of my Dad's tie collection. He's quite the snazzy man. I pull your thong off over your legs. Usher wailing, "Let me love you down," in the background. The memory of Tik and Tok fading in the air. I'm on my knees. You're on your head. Legs on the air. Spread like the Y in YMCA. Just like how Bishop Brennan would spread me little buttocks and massage me deep. I unbutton my jeans and kneel lower. Your hungry mouth reaches for my hard cock. Licking it upside down like some sort of deranged drunk wolf. Your pussy is wet and glistening for me, like a fresh dewy field at dawn. A farmer's delight. That's what you are. I squeeze plum juice over your clit and asshole. Licking your clit to your ass. My cock in your upside down mouth. We're on a Ferris wheel. An upside down 69. Just like how Mother Mary would want it. You sucking and licking. My cock getting harder and harder inside your wet mouth. Like a maths riddle stuck in an underwater cave. I love hearing you moan with my cock in your mouth as I press my tongue against your throbbing clit. "Good girl," I tell you, "You're a farmer." You barely hear me but moan louder. My tongue deep in your tight ass. Tastes like a plum. I rub your clit and eat your tight ass. You're moaning on my cock upside down. Your poor neck. Your wet pussy. Your tight ass. Your thighs shaking. Fingering. Licking. Rubbing. Clit throbbing. Ass tightening. Pussy soaking. Like a burst pipe. Gushing for me. I kiss and lick your clit as you start to cum hard. Holding you up as you cum like a dancer in my mouth. My cock fucking your wet mouth. Poor TikTok. Lovely wet cock. I take a plum and press it against your tight ass. Slowly sliding it inside. Your tight plum ass. I stand up and listen to Usher wail. I hope he's on repeat. I slide my cock inside your upside down pussy. Your wet ass potato, tight and sloppy, like an Irish uncle at a wedding just after finding out the free bar is over. I'm standing over you doing a headstand fucking you deep. Your ass squeezing the plum. Your cum and my precum. Dripping down your body. Your hot stomach. Your savage nipples. Hard with plum cum. I slap your ass "Good fucking girl." Bishop Brennan pops into my head and says "Drive it home for the team." I grab your sexy ass and go deeper. Spanking you hard upside down. Your neck must be broken. But this is too hot. Your clit swollen and wet. Rubbing it as we fuck. You start to cum again and your ass squeezes the plum out. I cum hard with you. Shooting deep inside your pleasure pond. Fuck me pink. I see the stars and some stairs. You hot farmer fucker. I pull out and cum on your tight plum ass. I see your mouth aching and open. I kneel down and cum in your mouth. Shooting in your throat. On your tongue and lips. Watching my cum drip out of your plum ass pussy. Upside down. Defying gravity. Malibu is burning. TikTok is dead. Usher is wailing. It's sad. So sad. But fuck me pink, you're a hot fucking sugar plum fairy. You farm of delight.

HONEYCUM

It's Tuesday. That day of St. Bruno, patron saint of solitary confinement. A lovely man. You're not alone when you're with God, as he liked to say. So true. That's why I'm never alone when I masturbate. Always a bit gay with God in the room. Thanks, God. Malibu is burning. It's October 6th and 90 degrees. Trump is wheezing. His foundation is a mess. It's sad. So sad. But at least we're at brunch. And you're looking glorious. In your black crop top and black sweatpants. You hot fucking delight. A shoe full of joy. A wife full of surprises. Your yellow lingerie underneath has me turned on as I'm ordering. I wanted to fuck you in the car on the way here but you were starving. Your yellow bra and yellow g-string are dominating my mind though. Your hard nipples showing through your top as Pierre Felipe takes our order. Not sure why brunch on a Tuesday but the world is burning. So who cares? If you asked me to do coke off your tits on the table right now I would say, "Sorry, God," and do it. Nothing means anything. It's hot. We're boozing mimosas. And kissing. Wet drunk lips. We're at the back corner of Taste on

Melrose. It's quiet. No one can see. Except for Pierre Felipe. You got me hard asking for extra Benedict with your eggs Benedict. The mimosas are kicking in. Your clavicle looks hot. I tell you "Your clavicle looks hot." "Please don't call it that," you tell me, "I'm already turned on and that word isn't hot." You make a good point. "Come here," I tell you. You come and sit on my lap. Facing me. Feeling my hard cock through my jeans. Me kissing your collar bone and hard nipples through your top. You're the sexiest fucker. You take a drink of mimosa and spit it into my mouth. I kiss your wet champagne lips and spit it back into yours. Your nipples getting harder. Your hand stroking my cock. Mine rubbing your clit. Feeling your warm wet pussy through your pants. I take a drink and start kissing your boobs. Taking the right one out of your top. Your hard nipple in my mouth, like I'm an overgrown baby and you're my mother, sitting on my lap. It's hot. Like how Father Diarmuid used to make me sit on his lap saying Our Father when we were growing up. He would bite on my nipple if it got the words wrong. I used to love Sunday school. You're running your hands through my stunning hair as you grind on my cock. Nipple rock hard in my mouth. Opening my jeans. Spitting on my cock and stroking it. I take some honey off the table and rub a dab on your nipple. Sucking it slowly. Sliding my hand down your pants. Pulling your g-string to the side. Running my honey finger over your swollen honey clit. Soaking wet for me. You're a good girl. You take another drink and spit in my mouth again. I kiss you hard and spit back. Mimosa fuckers. Your dripping pussy on me. My rock hard cock being stroked, like Father Brendan stroking my hair after I showed him how quick I could take all my clothes off. He loved that game. I slide two inside your tight wet pussy and watch you bite your bottom lip. Sucking on your nipples as I finger your drenched pleasure pond. The sexiest pussy. The sexiest fucker. The hottest clavicle. I want your honeycum. I feel you sit up straight on me and fix your top. Pierre Felipe is back with our eggs. You stay on my lap smiling as he drops off the food. I'm pulling your pants down slowly. A napkin hiding how naked and wet you are. My cock rubbing off your wet swollen clit. You biting on your lip and nodding as Pierre Felipe asks "Anything else I can get you?" "No that's grand cheers," I tell him, sliding my ponder pipe inside your cabbage patch. You're breathing deep and barely able to hold back a moan. I love you horny and wild for me. You are my kink, you sexy fuck. Your weapon body and savage hair. Your perfect ass and soaking pussy. You're the dream. And Jesus, that clavicle. You start grinding on my cock slowly as Pierre Felipe walks away, like an expensive coffee machine on me cock beans. "Ask him for more mimosas," I tell you. "Pierre! Oh Pierre!" you moan out into the air, like you're in the Sound of Music. Pierre turns around and asks "Oui?" You're enjoying riding my cock too much. Fucking me while looking Pierre in the eye. Making people uncomfortable. Eye contact with the innocents. Breathing heavy. Stomach going deep. My cock deep inside. Your clit throbbing. You're my fucking kink. "More mimosas, please," you whimper out, sounding like Casper the drunk horny ghost. Pierre nods and walks away. You start riding my cock full on. Hand choking your neck. Nipple in my mouth. Mimosa dripping down your body. Like an ice cream dripping down Father Tony's fingers. He loved to have them licked. You suck on my fingers as you start to cum on my cock. Eggs benedick all over. Riding me harder and harder. You're a good fucking girl. Kissing me hard. I choke you harder. Slap your sexy face. Feel you cum some more. You grab a flute and chug the last of the champagne. Get on your knees between my legs and spit the mimosa on my cock. Looking at me as you suck my drunk cock, like a drunk naked Uncle at Christmas time, wet and slippery and hard to understand. Stroking and spitting on it. Underneath the table. The brunch on top. The hot wife below. You sexy fucker. Feeling me getting closer and closer. Opening your mouth as I cum on your lips and face. Swallowing my cock as I shoot deep inside your throat. Fucking your mouth as I cum even more. Fuck me pink. You're the hottest brunch. You show me my cum on your tongue and smile, then swallow it all. You stand up and kiss me. I turn you around and bend you over the table. Spreading your ass cheeks as I taste your mimosa ass. Moaning over the eggs as my tongue slides inside. I run my tongue along your pussy to your clit. You taste like honeycum. The fucking hottest. I spank your ass and pull up your pants. You sit on the other side of the table just as Pierre Felipe returns. He's our voyeur now. Malibu is burning. Trump is gasping. It's 90 degrees in October. It's sad. So sad. But you're the hottest mimosa fucker. And still have cum on your lips. I'll lick it off later at the next bar. You hot egg of delight.

ACKNOWLEDGMENTS

Thanks to everyone who supported the sextpoems by paying for one or contributing to more, you helped to create this glorious mess. Thanks to Robbie for the foreword, truly stunning. Thanks to Michael for the glowing blurb, delighted I saved your marriage. Thanks to the one guy before who emailed me and said "Your a cumt." Very inspiring. Thanks to Shary for the cover design and proofreading. Thanks to Liz for the author photo. And last but alas not least, thanks to everyone who buys the book, ye harny, harny souls.

BOOKS BY MARK HAYES

RanDumb: The Adventures of an Irish Guy in L.A.
RanDumber: The Continued Adventures of an Irish Guy in L.A.
PreDumb: Before I Came to L.A.

Mark can be found on
Instagram @themarkhayes
Twitter @trickaduu
www.markhayes.tv

Made in the U.S.A.
Los Angeles, CA

Made in the USA
Las Vegas, NV
20 January 2021

16243274R00134